Investigations
Physics
A *First* Course

Tom Hsu, Ph.D.

A member of
School Specialty
Science

D1361384

About the Author

Dr. Thomas C. Hsu is a nationally recognized innovator in science and math education and the founder of CPO Science (formerly Cambridge Physics Outlet). He holds a Ph.D. in Applied Plasma Physics from the Massachusetts Institute of Technology (MIT), and has taught students from elementary, secondary and college levels across the nation. He was nominated for MIT's Goodwin medal for excellence in teaching and has received numerous awards from various state agencies for his work to improve science education. Tom has personally worked with more than 12,000 K-12 teachers and administrators and is well known as a consultant, workshop leader and developer of curriculum and equipment for inquiry-based learning in science and math. With CPO Science, Tom has published textbooks in physical science, integrated science, and also written fifteen curriculum Investigation guides that accompany CPO Science equipment. Along with the CPO Science team, Tom is always active, developing innovative new tools for teaching and learning science.

Physics A First Course Investigations
Copyright © 2005, 2008 CPO Science, a member of School Specialty Science
ISBN-10: 1-58892-142-5
ISBN-13: 978-1-58892-142-0
1 2 3 4 5 6 7 8 9 - QWE - 11 10 09 08 07

CPO Science
80 Northwest Boulevard
Nashua, NH 03063
http://www. cposcience.com
Printed and Bound in the United States of America

CPO SCIENCE STAFF

Tom Hsu, Ph.D – Author

Ph.D., Applied Plasma Physics, Massachusetts Institute of Technology

Nationally recognized innovator in science who promotes the teaching of physics through inquiry. Dr. Hsu founded CPO Science to create innovative hands-on materials for teaching science and math.

Lynda Pennell – Educational Products, Executive Vice President

B.A., English, M.Ed., Administration, Reading Disabilities, Northeastern University; CAGS Media, University of Massachusetts, Boston

Nationally known in high school restructuring and for integrating academic and career education. Served as the director of an urban school with 17 years teaching/administrative experience.

Scott Eddleman – Project Manager and Principle Writer

B.S., Biology, Southern Illinois University; M.Ed, Harvard University.

Taught for thirteen years in urban and rural settings; nationally known as a trainer of inquiry-based science/math project-based instruction; curriculum development consultant.

Mary Beth Hughes – Curriculum Specialist and Principle Writer

B.S., Marine Biology, College of Charleston; M.S., Biological Sciences, University of Rhode Island

Taught science and math at an innovative high school; has expertise in scientific research and inquiry-based teaching methods.

Erik Benton – Professional Development Specialist and Principle Investigation Editor

B.F.A. University of Massachusetts

Taught for eight years in public and private schools, focusing on inquiry and experiential learning environments.

Stacy Kissel – Consulting Principle writer

B.S., Civil and Environmental Engineering, Carnegie Mellon University; M.Ed., Physics Education, Boston College

Nine years teaching experience physics, math and integrated science.

Bruce Holloway – Senior Creative Designer

Pratt Institute, N.Y.; Boston Museum School of Fine Arts

Expertise in product design, advertising, and three-dimensional exhibit design. Commissioned for the New Hampshire Duck Stamp for 1999 and 2003.

Polly Crisman – Graphic Manager, Designer and Illustrator

B.F.A., University of New Hampshire

Graphic artist with expertise in advertising and marketing design, freelance illustrating, and caricature art.

Sonja Taylor – Consulting Editor

B.S., Chemistry, Stephen F. Austin State University

Taught chemistry and biology for four years. Expertise in teaching with inquiry and technology.

EQUIPMENT DESIGN

Thomas Narro – Product Design, Senior Vice President

B.S., Mechanical engineering, Rensselaer Polytechnic Institute

Accomplished design and manufacturing engineer; experienced consultant in corporate reengineering and industrial-environmental acoustics.

Dave Zucker – Industrial Designer

B.A., Physics, Brandeis University

Talented designer with a strong background in physics and problem solving. Also contributed to several connections articles.

Greg Krekorian – Production Manager

A.S. Northeastern University in Industrial Management and program certified in Demand Flow Technology

Has twelve years of supervisory experience and works with product engineering on the development and implementation of product lines.

Kerry Gavin – Quality Control and Purchasing Manager

Responsible for quality control and purchasing and works with product engineering on all new development. Kerry has been assuring total quality of CPO Science equipment for ten years.

CONSULTANTS

James Travers – Graphic designer and animator

Associate Degree of Applied Business and Commercial Art, Akron University

Has held positions as graphic designer, art department manager, and currently is a commissioned painter.

Tracy Morrow – Framemaker Expert, Technical Editor, Technical Trainer

B.A., English, Texas A&M University; M.A., English, Sam Houston State University

Taught middle school in Houston, Texas, and English at Tomball College; has also worked as a technical writer and trainer in many industries.

Investigations Pages

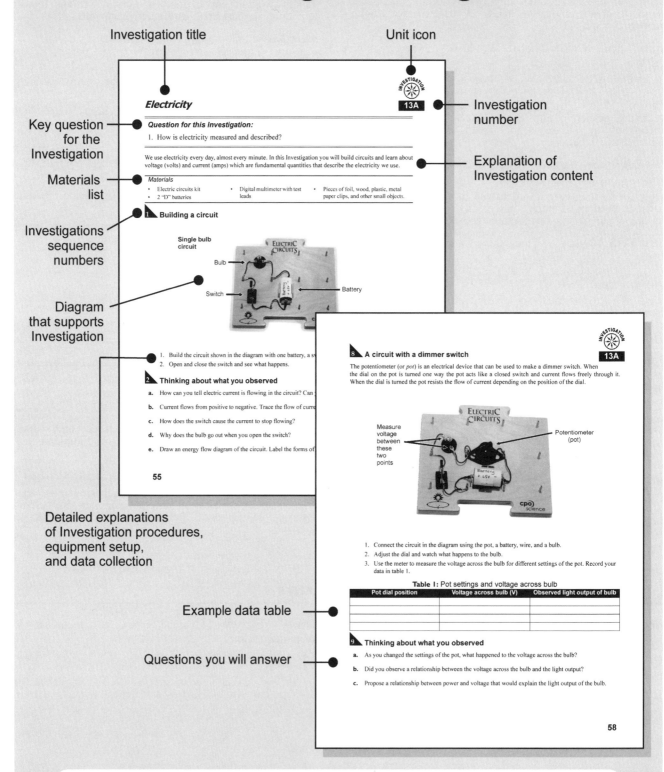

Investigation title

Unit icon

Key question for the Investigation

Materials list

Investigations sequence numbers

Diagram that supports Investigation

Detailed explanations of Investigation procedures, equipment setup, and data collection

Example data table

Questions you will answer

Investigation number

Explanation of Investigation content

Electricity

Question for this Investigation:

1. How is electricity measured and described?

We use electricity every day, almost every minute. In this Investigation you will build circuits and learn about voltage (volts) and current (amps) which are fundamental quantities that describe the electricity we use.

Materials

- Electric circuits kit
- 2 "D" batteries
- Digital multimeter with test leads
- Pieces of foil, wood, plastic, metal paper clips, and other small objects.

1. Building a circuit

Single bulb circuit

Bulb

Switch

Battery

1. Build the circuit shown in the diagram with one battery, a s...
2. Open and close the switch and see what happens.

2. Thinking about what you observed

a. How can you tell electric current is flowing in the circuit? Can...

b. Current flows from positive to negative. Trace the flow of curre...

c. How does the switch cause the current to stop flowing?

d. Why does the bulb go out when you open the switch?

e. Draw an energy flow diagram of the circuit. Label the forms of...

55

---

8. A circuit with a dimmer switch

13A

The potentiometer (or *pot*) is an electrical device that can be used to make a dimmer switch. When the dial on the pot is turned one way the pot acts like a closed switch and current flows freely through it. When the dial is turned the pot resists the flow of current depending on the position of the dial.

Measure voltage between these two points

Potentiometer (pot)

1. Connect the circuit in the diagram using the pot, a battery, wire, and a bulb.
2. Adjust the dial and watch what happens to the bulb.
3. Use the meter to measure the voltage across the bulb for different settings of the pot. Record your data in table 1.

Table 1: Pot settings and voltage across bulb

Pot dial position	Voltage across bulb (V)	Observed light output of bulb

9. Thinking about what you observed

a. As you changed the settings of the pot, what happened to the voltage across the bulb?

b. Did you observe a relationship between the voltage across the bulb and the light output?

c. Propose a relationship between power and voltage that would explain the light output of the bulb.

58

NOTE: All data and answers to questions will be written on a separate fill-in answer sheet.

Table of Contents

Equipment Setup

Projects

Time, Distance, and Speed

Question for this Investigation:

How is motion described and measured in physics?

This Investigation is about speed and motion. You will use a precise Timer and photogates to create a graph of motion that will allow you to predict what will happen even before you do it!

Materials

- Energy car and track
- Clay
- Timer and 2 photogates
- #33 rubber band

 Using the timer as a stopwatch

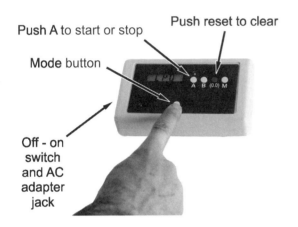

Push A to start or stop
Push reset to clear
Mode button
Off - on switch and AC adapter jack

1. Set the timer to **stopwatch**.
2. Start and stop the stopwatch with the "**A**" button.
3. Reset the stopwatch to zero with the "**O**" button.

The electronic timer allows us to make accurate, precise measurements of time. The timer performs many different functions. The first function to try is **stopwatch**. Use the mode button (1) to move the light under the word stopwatch.

A stopwatch measures a **time interval**. The stopwatch is started and stopped with the "**A**" button (2). The display shows time in seconds up to 60 seconds, then changes to show minutes: seconds for times longer than one minute.

The time it takes a signal to go from your brain to move a muscle is called **reaction time**. Reaction time varies from person to person and can be affected by factors like tiredness or caffeine intake.

Practice taking measurements with the stopwatch; then estimate the approximate reaction time of an average student.

2 Mixed units for time

Time is often given in mixed units including hours, minutes, and seconds. Mixed units are often written as shown in the diagrams below. Convert each one (a-c) to seconds.

Arrange the following times from smallest to largest:

a)

3 hours, 45 minutes, 16 seconds

b)

1 minute, 45.55 seconds

c)

1 hour, 6 minutes, 1 second

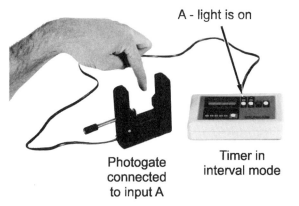
3 ▸ Using the photogates

A photogate allows us to use a light beam to start and stop the timer. When the timer is in interval mode, it uses photogates to control the clock.

Use a finger to break the light beam

A - light is on

Photogate connected to input A

Timer in interval mode

1. Connect a single photogate to the "**A**" input with a cord.

2. Select **interval** on the timer.

3. Push the "**A**" button and the "**A**" light should come on and stay on.

4. Try blocking the light beam with your finger and observe what happens to the timer. Because it is used for so many measurements, you need to figure out how the photogate and timer work together. Try your own experiments until you can answer the questions.

4 ▸ How the photogate works

a. Exactly what do you do to start and stop the timer? Be very specific in your answer. Someone who has never seen the photogate before should be able to read your answer and know what to do.

b. If you block the light beam several times in a row, does the time add or does the timer start at zero every time you break the beam? Your answer should provide observations that back up what you say. For example, "the timer does _____ because_____." Fill in the blanks with what you think based on what you observed.

5 ▸ Two photogates

The timer can be used with two photogates. Photogate A is connected to the A input and photogate B is connected to the B input. What the timer displays depends on the lights above the buttons. Pushing the A or B buttons toggles the A or B light on or off. Do your own experiments until you can fill in Table 1.

Table 1: Timer and photogate rules

A light	B light	How do you start the timer?	How do you stop the timer?	What time interval does the timer display?
On	Off			
Off	On			
On	On			
Off	Off			

6 ▸ Thinking about what you observed

a. Describe a way to measure the speed of a toy car using two photogates and a meter stick.

b. Describe a way to measure the speed of a toy car using one photogate and a meter stick.

c. What does the red Reset button do?

7 ▲ Constant speed

Setting up the straight track

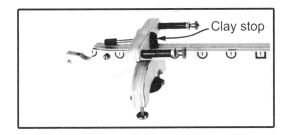

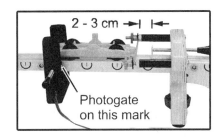

1. Put the track together as shown in the diagram. Use one rubber band on the launching end and a ball of clay on the catching end to stop the car.

2. Adjust the stop so the rubber band has 2 - 3 cm of deflection. Put a photogate on the mark just ahead of the car. Practice launching the car until you can get 3 successive photogate times to within 0.0010 seconds of each other.

3. Put two photogates on the track. Adjust the height of the leveling feet until the car has the same speed passing through both photogates.

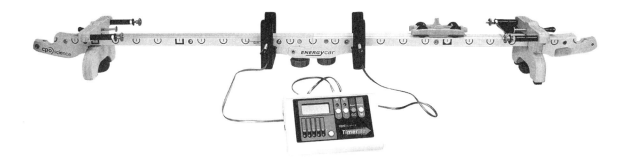

4. Be careful not to disturb the track once you get it set up level.

8 ▲ Thinking about what you observed

a. Describe how the photogate measurements prove that the car has constant speed, or nearly constant speed.

b. Calculate the speed of the car in meters per second (m/sec).

9 ◢ Position versus time

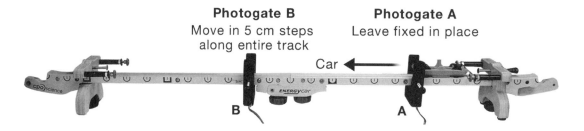

Photogate B
Move in 5 cm steps
along entire track

Photogate A
Leave fixed in place

Car ←

B   A

1. Move photogate A near the start so the car breaks the light beam just after it is launched.
2. Move photogate B to different positions 5 cm apart along the track (measure position).
3. For every position of photogate B, record the time through the beam at photogates A and B and also the time from A to B.
4. Take at least 8 data points along the track being careful to launch the car the same way every time. Use photogate A to test whether you should keep the data from a trial or do it over.

Table 2: Position versus time data

Position (cm)	Time through photogate A (sec.)	Time through photogate B (sec.)	Time from photogate A to B (sec.)

10 ◢ Thinking about what you observed

a. Draw a graph showing the position of the car on the vertical (y) axis and the time since the car was released on the horizontal (x) axis. The time you want is the time from photogate A to B.

b. What shape does the position versus time graph have? Describe the line or curve that you produce.

c. Calculate the average speed of the car in m/sec from the graph or your data.

d. How long would it take the car to travel a distance of 2 meters if it traveled at the speed you calculated in 10c?

Systems, Energy and Change

Questions for this Investigation:

1. Why do things change?
2. Why do things change by only a certain amount?

A system is a group of objects and influences that are related to each other and affect each other. Energy measures the ability of a system to change itself or other systems. This investigation is about systems and energy.

Materials

- Car and track
- Clay
- Timer and photogates
- Rubber band
- Physics stand

1 ▶ Making a system

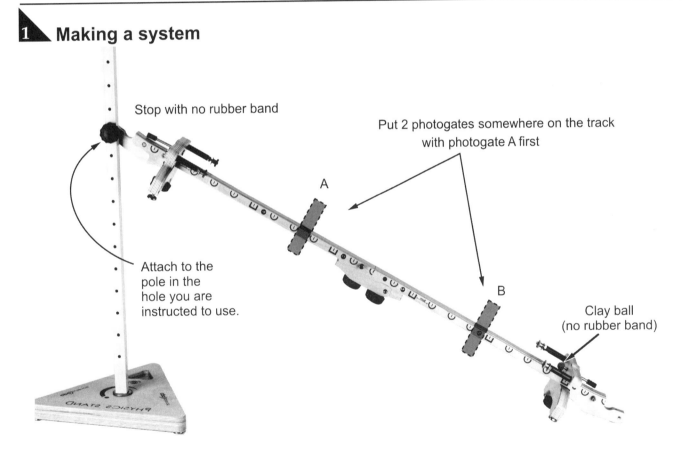

Stop with no rubber band

Put 2 photogates somewhere on the track with photogate A first

A

B

Attach to the pole in the hole you are instructed to use.

Clay ball (no rubber band)

1. Set up the track as a long straight hill. Your teacher will tell you which hole in the stand to attach the track.
2. Attach two photogates along the track, with photogate A higher up the hill.
3. Drop the car several times and measure the time it takes to roll from photogate A to photogate B.

2 Questions for the experiment

a. What is speed and how can it be measured with two photogates in this experiment?

b. Different cars are rolling on tracks with different angles. Which car should go the fastest? Which car should go the slowest?

c. Which car should have the shortest time from photogate A to photogate B? Which should have the longest time?

 3 What do you observe

Each group should drop the car and record the time it takes to get from photogate A to photogate B. Use Table 1 to record the times in the Trial #1 column. Leave the third column blank for now.

Table 1: Speed data

Hole #	Trial #1 Time in seconds	Trial #2 Time in seconds

 4 Thinking about what you observed

a. Did the times in Table 1 agree with your hypothesis? Explain in one sentence why or why not.

b. What objects and influences should be "in" your system if you want to investigate the motion of the car?

c. Name two things that should not be in your system since they do not influence the motion.

d. What is a variable? What variables affect the motion of the car in your system? Make a list of the variables (Hint: there are at least 6 important ones).

e. What variable is being tested in your class experiment (the experimental variable)? How do you know?

f. What should be done with the other variables which are not the experimental variable? Why?

 5 A better experiment

1. Each group should place the photogates in the same places on the track. Other variables may also need to be controlled.
2. Re-run the experiment and record the times for each group in Table 1 using the third column (Trial #2)

 6 Thinking about what you observed

a. Did the new times for the second trial of the experiment agree with your hypothesis about which track should have the fastest car? Explain in one sentence why or why not.

6

7 Energy in the system

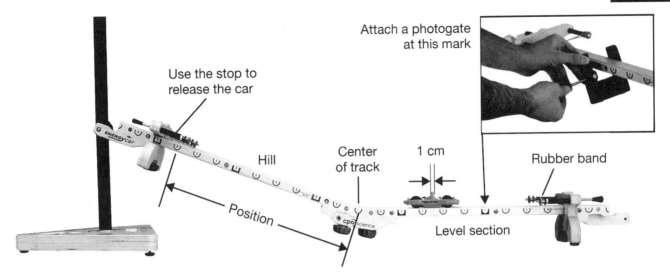

Attach a photogate at this mark

Use the stop to release the car

Hill

Center of track

1 cm

Rubber band

Position

Level section

1. Set up the track with the steeper hill and a level section.

2. Put a photogate near the middle of the level section.

3. Drop the car from different heights on the hill using the screw on the stop to provide a repeatable starting point. Measure and record position from the center of the track.

4. Use the photogate to measure the speed of the car before and after bouncing off the rubber band. The speed of the car is the width of the flag divided by the time it takes the flag to pass through the beam of the photogate (measure the width of the flag in cm).

5. Drop the car from different heights to get several different speeds.

Table 2: Energy data

Drop position (cm from center)	Before rubber band		After rubber band	
	Time through photogate (sec)	Speed (cm/sec)	Time through photogate (sec)	Speed (cm/sec)

8 Thinking about what you observed

a. If you drop the car from a certain height does it ever go higher after bouncing off the rubber band?

b. If the car has a certain speed going into the rubber band does it ever have a greater speed after bouncing off? (Hint: use the timer's memory button.)

c. When you drop the car from a certain height it reaches a certain speed at the photogate. If you launch the car with the same speed back up the hill, does the car ever get higher than the height at which you first dropped it? (try this experiment)

d. In one paragraph, explain how the answers to a, b, and c are explained using the idea of energy.

The Law of Inertia

Question for this Investigation:

Why are heavier objects harder to start moving or stop from moving?

This Investigation is about mass and inertia. Inertia is the property of an object that resists changes in motion. Inertia comes from mass. Objects with more mass have proportionally more inertia. In this Investigation, you will explore Newton's first law, the law of inertia.

Materials

- Car and track
- Physics stand
- Timer and 1 photogate
- Clay and rubber band
- Mass balance
- 3 metal balls

1 ▶ Launching cars of different mass

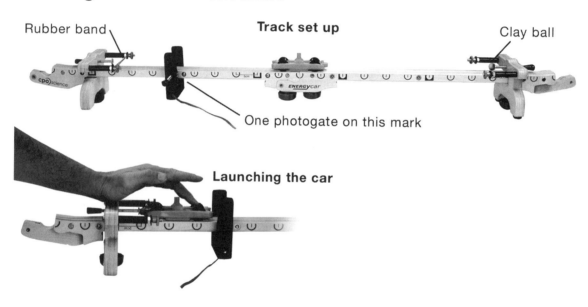

1. Set up the long straight track with a rubber band one end and a clay ball on the other end.
2. Put one photogate about 10 cm away from the rubber band.
3. Launch cars of four different masses and observe their speeds when they pass through the photogate. Use the screw to launch the car using the same deflection of the rubber band each time. This means the same force is applied to each car.
4. Measure the mass of the car with 0, 1, 2, and 3 steel balls.

Table 1: Constant force data

Mass of car (kg)	Time through photogate (sec)	Speed (m/sec)

8

2 ▶ Thinking about what you observed

a. Use Table 1 to graph the speed of the car (y) against the mass (x).

b. Why did the speed change when the same launching force from the rubber band was applied to cars of different mass? How do your observations support your answer?

3 ▶ Inertia and weight

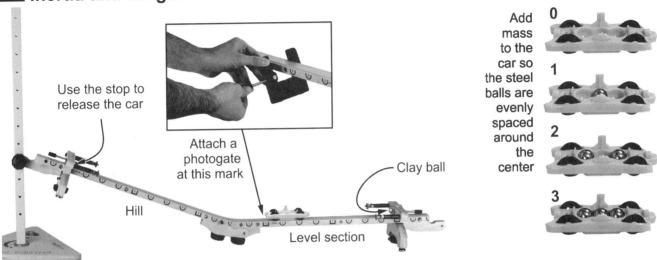

Use the stop to release the car

Attach a photogate at this mark

Clay ball

Hill

Level section

Add mass to the car so the steel balls are evenly spaced around the center

0
1
2
3

1. Set up the track with a hill and a straight section. Attach the photogate on the flat section.
2. Use the upper stop to drop the car from the same place every time.
3. Drop cars of 4 different masses from the same height on the hill. Use the photogate to measure the speed of the car at the same place each time.

Table 2: Constant height data

Mass of car (kg)	Time through photogate (sec)	Speed (m/sec)

4 ▶ Thinking about what you observed

a. What force makes the car go down the hill? What property of matter does this force act upon?

b. Does increasing the mass of the car increase its speed by a proportional amount? Does the speed decrease with increasing mass? Does the speed stay about the same, no matter what the mass?

c. Discuss and propose an explanation for why changing the mass has a very different effect on the speed when gravity provides the force compared to when the force is provided by a rubber band.

d. Research and define the terms "inertia", "weight" and "mass". Write 2-3 sentences that describe how these three concepts are similar and how they are different.

Newton's Second Law

Questions for this Investigation:

1. What is force?
2. What is the relationship between force and motion?

Newton's second law is probably the most widely used relationship in all of physics. It tells us how much force is needed to cause an object's speed to increase or decrease at a given rate. It also allows us to figure out how much force is involved by watching the motion of an object change. In this Investigation, you will explore Newton's second law by measuring the change in speed as a function of force and mass.

Materials

- Car and track
- Clay
- Timer and photogates
- Mass balance

1 ▶ Looking at the motion along the track

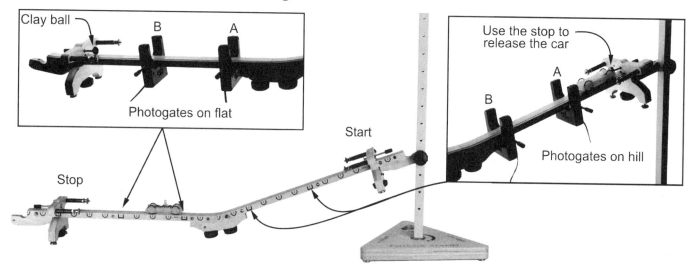

1. Set up the track with a hill and a level section.
2. Put two photogates 20 cm apart on the level section. Adjust the level of the track until the car has constant speed on the level part (same time through photogates A and B). Roll the car and record the three photogate times in table 1. Use the stop so you can repeat the same release position.
3. Put the two photogates 20 cm apart on the down hill section of the track. Roll the car starting from the same place and record the three photogate times (Table 1).
4. Calculate the speed of the car at photogates A and B.

Table 1: Speed data

	Time photogate A (sec)	Time photogate B (sec)	Time from A to B (sec)	Speed at A (m/sec)	Speed at B (m/sec)
Level section					
Down hill section					

2 ▶ Thinking about what you observed

a. Where is there a net force acting on the car? How do you know?

b. Where is there zero net force on the car? How do you know?

c. Can you have constant speed with zero net force? What experimental data support your answer?

d. Write down a formula for the acceleration of the car in terms of the speeds at photogates A and B and the time from A to B.

e. Calculate the acceleration of the car in m/sec^2 on both the level section and the downhill section.

f. Explain the difference in acceleration between the level and downhill sections using Newton's second law and the concept of force.

3 ▶ Speed and time graphs

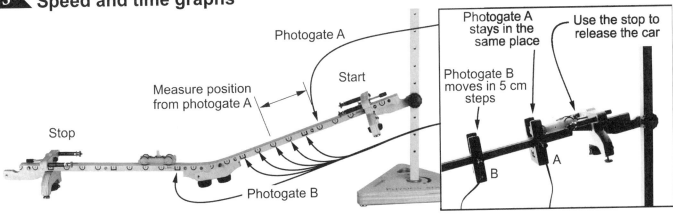

1. Set photogate A near the top of the hill and leave it there.

2. Move photogate B along the track in 5 cm steps and record its position relative to photogate A. Measure the 3 photogate times for each position of photogate B.

3. Measure the mass of the car.

Table 2: Speed versus time data

Position (cm)	Time through A (sec)	Time through B (sec)	Time from A to B (sec)	Speed at A (m/sec)	Speed at B (m/sec)

4 ▶ Thinking about what you observed

a. Draw the graph of speed vs. time for the track. For the x-axis use the time from photogate A to B.

b. Use Newton's second law to calculate the force acting on the car at each position. Measure the acceleration from your speed vs. time graph. Where does the force come from?

c. Draw the graph of force vs. time and compare this graph to the speed vs. time graph. What relationship is there between the two graphs?

d. Explain how speed and acceleration are different using your speed vs. time graph as an example.

Momentum and the Third Law

Question for this Investigation:

What makes moving objects keep going at the same speed in the same direction?

When you throw a ball it goes in the direction you threw it and does not suddenly turn one way or another unless a big force is applied. If you did try to deflect the ball you would find that for every force you apply to the ball, the ball exerts an equal and opposite force against your hand. This Investigation is about momentum and Newton's third law: the law of action and reaction.

Materials

- Energy car and track (2 cars)
- 4 metal balls
- Timer and photogates
- Rubber bands
- Mass balance
- Clay

 Making a collision

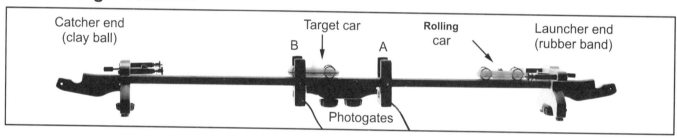

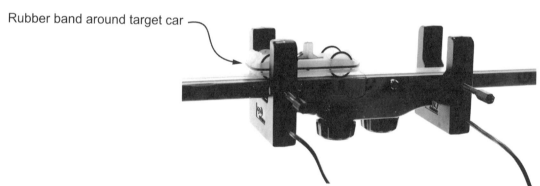

Rubber band around target car

1. Set up the long straight track with a rubber band launcher on one stop and a clay ball on the other. Use the photogates to adjust the track so it is level (same time through A and B).
2. Put a photogate on either side of the center. Photogate A should be closest to the rubber band.
3. Place one car with between the photogates. This is the target car. The pointy end of the car should be facing the launching end of the track. Place 1 steel ball in this car.
4. Wrap a rubber band around the second car and place it on the launching end of the track. This is the rolling car. This car should also have 1 steel ball and should have its pointy end facing the launcher and the "V" end facing the target car. The cars will collide with each other at the center of the track.
5. Launch the rolling car at the target car. After the collision, record the times through photogates A and B. You may have to use the memory button to see the time if the rolling car goes through twice (bounces back). Observe the direction and motion of both cars after the collision.

2 Thinking about what you observed.

Table 1: Collision data

Mass of target car (kg)	Mass of rolling car (kg)	Rolling car before collision		Rolling car after collision		Target car after collision	
		Photogate (sec)	Speed (m/sec)	Photogate (sec)	Speed (m/sec)	Photogate (sec)	Speed (m/sec)

a. Consider two colliding cars of equal mass. Describe in words the motion of the two cars before and after the collision.

b. The target car must exert a force on the rolling car to stop it. How strong is this force relative to the force the rolling car exerts on the target car to get it moving? What experimental evidence supports your answer?

c. Look up Newton's third law and state how it applies to the collision of the two cars.

3 Momentum

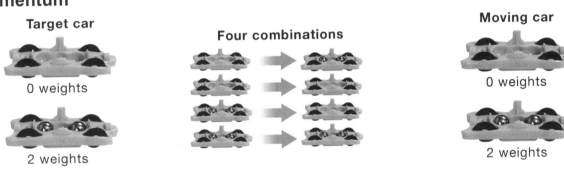

Target car
0 weights
2 weights

Four combinations

Moving car
0 weights
2 weights

1. Try the experiment with the four combinations of mass shown above. Add the data to Table 1.
2. Try the experiment for several different speeds of the moving car. Add the date to Table 1.

4 Thinking about what you observed

a. Describe the motion of the two cars when the target car has more mass than the rolling car.

b. Describe the motion of the two cars when the target car has less mass than the rolling car.

c. Research and write down a formula for the momentum of a moving object. State what each of the variables are and what units they have.

d. Calculate the total momentum of the two cars before and after each collision. Be sure to remember that momentum can be positive or negative depending on the direction of motion.

e. Research and write down the law of conservation of momentum. Describe how your data either support or do not support this law.

Conservation of Energy

Question for this Investigation:

What limits how much a system may change?

A car launched up the hill at a given speed will never go higher than a certain point. A car rolling downhill will only reach a certain speed. Why? The answer is that nature keeps an exact balance of energy. Speed uses one form of energy and height uses another. This Investigation explores the exchange of energy.

Materials

- Car and track
- Physics stand
- CPO timer and photogates
- Mass balance
- Clay
- String
- Meter stick
- Metal balls

1 ▶ Energy exchange from potential to kinetic

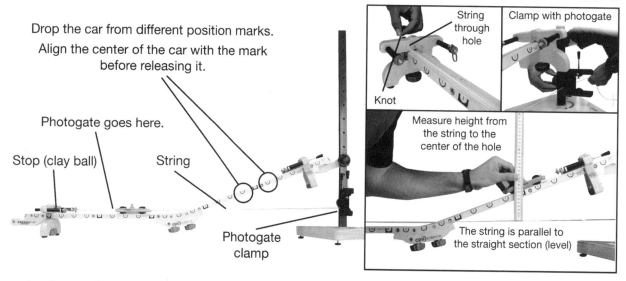

Drop the car from different position marks. Align the center of the car with the mark before releasing it.

Photogate goes here.

Stop (clay ball)   String

Photogate clamp

String through hole

Knot

Clamp with photogate

Measure height from the string to the center of the hole

The string is parallel to the straight section (level)

1. Set up the track with the steeper hill and a level section. Make the level section as level as you can.
2. Thread a string though the hole in the lower stop and use a photogate to clamp the other end of the string to the stand. Adjust the string so it is parallel to the level section of the track.
3. Put a photogate at the bottom of the hill on the level section.
4. Drop the car from each 5-cm mark on the hill and measure the speed with the photogate. Measure the height of the car from the string to the center of the car.
5. Measure the mass of the car. Do the experiment for two different masses.

Table 1: Downhill data

Drop Height (m)	Mass of car (kg)	Photogate time (sec)	Speed (m/sec)

2 **Thinking about what you observed**

a. Graph the speed of the car vs. the height. Use different symbols for different masses.

b. What does the graph tell you about the relationship between speed and height?

3 **Analyzing the data**

a. Use the formula for potential energy to fill in the second column of Table 2.

b. Use energy conservation to derive a formula for the speed of the car in terms of the energy it has at the start. (Hint: your formula should include only two variables, velocity and height.)

c. Use the formula you just derived to fill in the column for the predicted speed of the car.

d. Plot the curve for the predicted speed on the same graph as you made in part 2a above.

Table 2: Energy data and predicted speeds

Drop Height (m)	Potential energy (J)	Predicted speed (m/sec)	Measured speed from Table 1 (m/sec)

4 **Thinking about what you observed**

a. Explain the relationship between speed and height using the idea of energy conservation.

b. Explain any difference between the predicted and measured speeds. If there is a difference, what does it tell you about the energy of the car as it rolls along the track?

c. Did changing the mass have a significant effect on the relationship between height and speed? How does your data support your answer?

d. Let the car roll downhill, bounce off the rubber band and go back up hill again. Does it reach the same height as it was dropped from? Explain why or why not using the idea of energy conservation.

e. Challenge experiment. Use a rubber band to launch the car uphill so it goes through the photogate with the same speed as it had going down. You won't be able to get it precisely the same, but come as close as you can. If the speeds are the same, the car's kinetic energy is also the same. Does the car reach the same height on the hill that it was dropped from to get the same speed in part 1? Explain any difference using the idea of energy lost to friction.

Force, Work, and Machines

Question for this Investigation:

How do simple machines affect work?

Machines are things humans invent to make tasks easier. Simple machines work by using directly applied forces. Using only muscle power, simple machines allowed humans to build the great pyramids and other monuments. This Investigation is about how simple machines use force to accomplish a task.

Materials

- Ropes and pulleys
- Spring scales
- Physics stand
- Four steel weights
- Meter stick

1 Building a simple machine

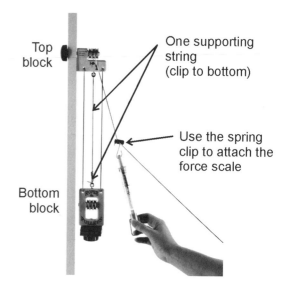

Measuring the input force

1. Attach four weights to the bottom block. Use a spring scale to measure the weight of the bottom block and record it as the output force.
2. Attach the top block near the top of the physics stand.
3. Thread the yellow string over one or more of the pulleys of the top and bottom pulley blocks. The yellow string can be clipped to either the top block or the bottom block.
4. Build combinations with 1, 2, 3, 4, 5, and 6 supporting strings directly supporting the bottom block. (Hint: 1, 3, and 5 have the string clipped to the bottom block. 2, 4, and 6 have the string clipped to the top block)
5. Use a force scale to measure the force needed to slowly lift the bottom block for different combinations of supporting strings.

Safety Tip: Don't pull sideways, or you can tip the stand over!

Table 1: Input and Output Forces

Number of supporting strings	Input force (newtons)	Output force (newtons)
1		
2		
3		

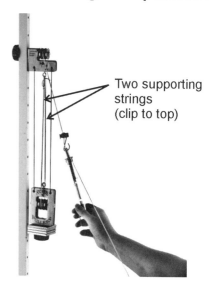

2 **Thinking about what you observed**

a. As you increase the number of supporting strings, what happens to the force needed to lift the bottom block?

b. Write a rule that relates the number of pulleys, input force, and output force.

c. Research the term "mechanical advantage." What does this mean for a simple machine?

d. Use your data from Table 1 to calculate the mechanical advantage for each arrangement of supporting strings.

3 **The input and output distance**

1. Use the marker stop (cord stop) to mark where the string leaves the top pulley.

2. Choose a distance that you will lift the bottom pulley during each trial of the experiment. This is the **output distance**. Your output distance should be at least 20 centimeters.

3. Pull the yellow string to lift the block your chosen distance.

4. Measure how much string length you had to pull to lift the block. This is the **input distance**.

5. Measure the input and output distances for each of the different configurations (1, 2, 3, 4, 5, and 6)

6. Copy your Input force and Output force data from part 1 into Table 2.

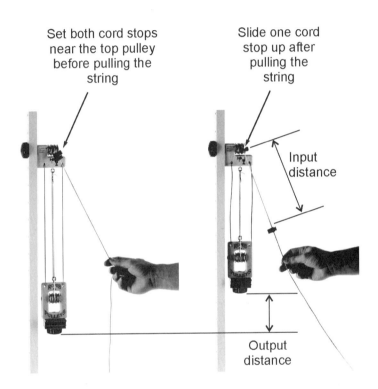

Set both cord stops near the top pulley before pulling the string

Slide one cord stop up after pulling the string

Input distance

Output distance

Measuring the input and output distance

Table 2: Force and Distance Data

Mechanical advantage	Output force (newtons)	Output distance (meters)	Input force (newtons)	Input distance (meters)
1				
2				
3				
4				

17

 Thinking about what you observed

a. As the mechanical advantage increases, what happens to the length of the string you have to pull to raise the block?

b. The word *work* is used in many different ways. For example, you *work* on science problems, your toaster doesn't *work*, or taking out the trash is too much *work*. In science, however, *work* has one specific meaning. Write one sentence that defines work in its scientific meaning.

c. You may have heard the saying, "nothing is free." Explain why this is true of the ropes and pulleys. (HINT: What do you trade for using less input force to lift the block?)

d. Use your data to calculate the work done on the block (the **output work**).

e. Next, use your data to calculate the work you did as you pulled on the string to lift the block. This is the **input work**.

Table 3: Output and Input Work

Mechanical advantage	Output work (joules)	Input work (joules)
1		
2		
3		
4		
5		
6		

f. For each mechanical advantage, how do output and input work compare?

g. Is output work ever greater than input work? Can you explain this?

h. Explain any differences between input and output work in your data.

Work and Energy

Question for this Investigation:

How does a system get energy?

Energy comes from somewhere. When you lift a box off the floor the increase in energy of the box comes from the work you do on the box. This Investigation looks into the conversion of work to energy.

Materials

- Car and track
- Physics stand
- Mass balance
- 10 N Force scale
- Metric ruler
- String

1 ▶ Measuring the work done

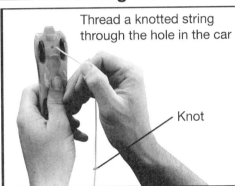

Thread a knotted string through the hole in the car

Knot

Pass the string under the notch just below the screw

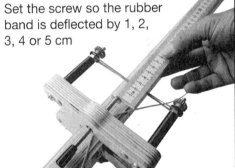

Set the screw so the rubber band is deflected by 1, 2, 3, 4 or 5 cm

Use a force scale to measure the force it takes to pull the car so it just touches the screw

1. Set up the long straight track with a rubber band at one end and a clay ball at the other end.
2. Adjust the threaded screw until the distance between the screw and the front of the rubber band is one centimeter (see diagram).
3. Tie a knot in the string and pass the string through the hole in the car and under the notch just below the screw. Tie a loop in the other end of the string.
4. Use a spring scale to measure the force when the car is just touching the screw.
5. Adjust the screw for distances of 2, 3, 4, and 5 centimeters. Measure the force for each distance. Record your measurements in Table 1.

Table 1: Force vs. distance data

Distance rubber band is stretched (mm)	Force (N)

2 Thinking about what you observed

a. Graph the force from the rubber band vs. the distance.

b. Write down a one sentence definition of work in physics.

c. You would like to know how much work the rubber band does on the car during a launch. Since the force changes with distance, use the graph to do some averaging. Divide your graph up into bars each representing one centimeter of distance. Make the height of each bar the average force over the distance interval covered by the bar. The area of each bar is the work done over that interval of distance. Your graph will have data out to 5 cm. The sample graph below shows data from 0 to 3 cm as a demonstration that you can follow for your entire graph.

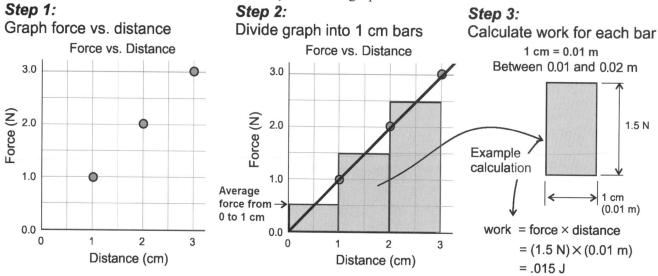

Step 1:
Graph force vs. distance

Step 2:
Divide graph into 1 cm bars

Step 3:
Calculate work for each bar

1 cm = 0.01 m
Between 0.01 and 0.02 m

work = force × distance
= (1.5 N) × (0.01 m)
= .015 J

d. To get the total work done on the car you need to add up all the work done as the rubber band straightens out and moves the car forward. Use the table below to calculate the work done.

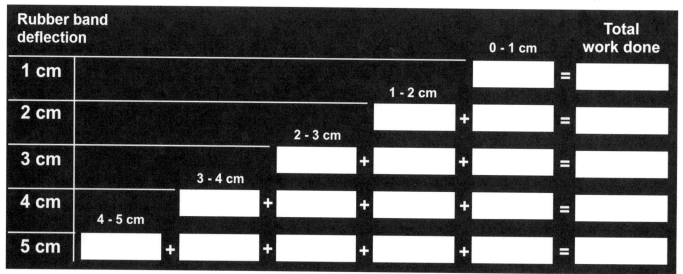

Rubber band deflection				0 - 1 cm	Total work done
1 cm					=
2 cm			1 - 2 cm	+	=
3 cm		2 - 3 cm	+	+	=
4 cm	3 - 4 cm	+	+	+	=
5 cm	4 - 5 cm +	+	+	+	=

e. Make a graph showing the work done on the *y*-axis and the deflection of the rubber band on the x-axis.

f. Assume all the work done becomes kinetic energy of the car. Derive a formula for the speed of the car that depends only on the car's mass and the work done by the rubber band.

 **Testing the theory**

Set the photogate just ahead of the flag when the rubber band is straight.

Launch the car at the same measured deflections for which you measured the force.

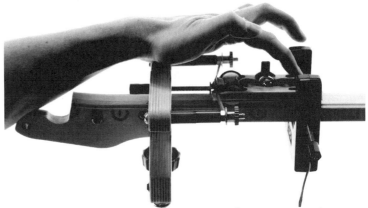

1. Put a photogate on the track so the flag on the car breaks the light beam about one centimeter after leaving the rubber band.
2. Use the adjustment screw to launch the car at the same measured deflections of the rubber band for which you measured the forces (1, 2, 3, 4, and 5 cm).
3. Measure the speed of the car for each deflection of the rubber band.
4. At each deflection, take data using cars with one steel ball of added mass. Record the speed in the column for "measured speed".

Table 2: Deflection, mass, and speed data

Deflection of rubber band (cm)	Mass of car (kg)	Photogate time (sec)	Measured Speed (m/sec)	Predicted Speed (m/sec)

 Thinking about what you observed

a. Use your formula to predict the speed the car should have at each combination of mass and deflection. Write the results in Table 2 in the column "predicted speed".

b. Graph the predicted speed of the car vs. the deflection of the rubber band. Draw a smooth curve through the plotted points. On the same graph, show the measured speeds.

c. Graph the measured speed of the car vs. the deflection of the rubber band on the same graph as part c.

d. Does your data support the theory that the energy of the car is equal to the work done by the rubber band? Your answer should provide evidence from your results and discuss possible sources of errors.

e. Use your theory to predict the speed if a car with 2 and 3 steel balls is launched at a deflection of 3 cm. Do the experiment and see if your prediction is accurate.

Equilibrium and Forces

Question for this Investigation:

What can we say about forces when nothing is moving?

When nothing is moving it does not mean there are no forces acting. It means things are in *equilibrium*. In equilibrium the total (net) force is zero. You can have as many forces as you wish, they just have to be arranged so the total is zero. This Investigation explores the concept of equilibrium using force scales.

Materials

- Steel washers (30)
- Four loops of string
- Balance
- A steel key ring
- 5-N, 10-N, and 20-N spring scales

 Making equilibrium

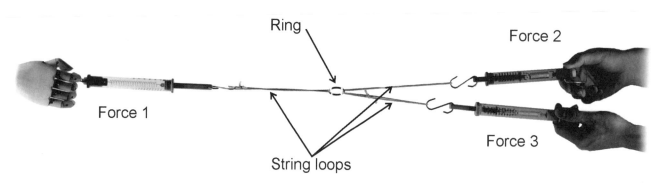

The ring is in equilibrium when it is not moving

Try to keep your spring scales as parallel as possible, not at an angle as in this illustration

1. Hold each spring scale vertically from its top loop and check to see that it is properly calibrated. If it needs to be adjusted, turn the nut at the top of the scale until it reads zero.
2. Attach three scales to the loops of string with the key ring in the middle.
3. Have three people each pull a scale, keeping the ring motionless with all the scales in a line.
4. Record the forces when 2 people are pulling against 1.
5. Try a few different combinations of scales and forces.

Table 1: Force data

Scale #1 (N)	Scale #2 (N)	Scale #3 (N)

2 ▸ Thinking about what you observed

a. What do your observations tell you about the relationship between the three forces acting on the ring?

b. Draw a diagram showing the forces acting on the ring as arrows. Make the length of each arrow proportional to the strength of each force. For example, 1 cm per N might be a reasonable length scale. This kind of diagram is called a *free body diagram*.

Example
free body diagram   15 N ⟵   ◯ ⟶ 10 N
                                       ⟶ 5 N

c. If the total force acting on an object is zero, what does Newton's second law say about the motion? Does the object have to be at rest?

3 ▸ The force of gravity

One of the ways we use equilibrium every day is to weigh things, including ourselves!

Measure the mass of each group of washers after you tie them to the string loop

Use a spring scale to measure the weight of each group of washers

1. Take a loop of string and attach 5 steel washers.
2. Use a calibrated force scale to measure the weight of the washers.
3. Measure the mass using a mass balance.
4. Repeat the experiment for 5, 10, 15, 20, 25, and 30 washers.

Table 2: Mass and weight data

Number of washers	Mass (kg)	Weight (N)

4 ▸ Thinking about what you observed

a. Draw a free body diagram showing the two forces acting on the group of washers.

b. The spring scale gives you one force, how do you know the other one?

c. Make a graph showing the weight in Newtons on the *y*-axis versus the mass in kilograms on the *x*-axis.

d. The strength of gravity is measured in N/kg. On the moon, the strength of gravity is 1.62 N/kg. That means a 1-kg object weighs 1.62 N on the Moon. Determine the strength of Earth's surface gravity from your graph.

Friction

Question for this Investigation:

How do we account for friction?

Friction is always present. Sometimes, we want friction. for example, between tires and the road. Other times we want to reduce friction. for example, putting oil on a bicycle chain. This Investigation explores some of the properties of friction.

Materials

- Car and track
- Timer and photogates
- Spring scales

 Sliding friction

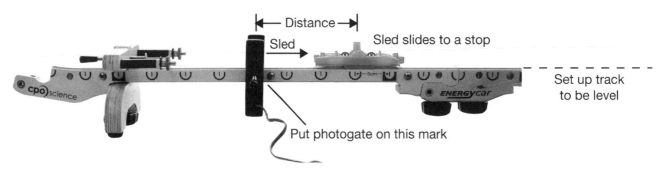

1. Set up the long straight track so the track is exactly level. Put a rubber band on one end and a clay ball on the other end.
2. Place a photogate on the mark just ahead of the flag on the car.
3. Launch the sled from the rubber band. Record the time it takes to pass through the photogate and also the distance the sled moves past the photogate before coming to a stop.
4. Change the mass of the sled by adding steel balls. Repeat the experiment for all four possible combinations of mass. Measure the mass for each trial.

Table 1: Force vs. mass data

Sled mass (kg)	Photogate time (sec)	Speed (m/sec)	Distance moved (m)	Kinetic energy (J)	Force of friction (N)

Analyzing the data

a. When the sled passes the photogate, you know its speed so you also know its kinetic energy. Use the mass and speed to calculate the kinetic energy for each trial.

b. Set the work done against friction equal to the sled's kinetic energy. Use this relationship to calculate the force of friction from the distance the sled moves past the photogate before stopping.

3 Rolling friction

Rolling friction is usually much smaller than sliding friction. You will use Newton's second law to calculate the force of rolling friction from the rate at which the car slows down (acceleration).

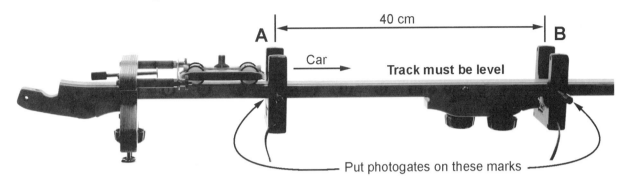

1. Put two photogates on the level track 40 cm apart as shown in the diagram.
2. Launch the car at different speeds and record the three times from the photogates.
3. Measure the mass and try the experiment for four different combinations of mass.

Table 2: Rolling friction data

Mass of car (kg)	Photogate A time (sec)	Photogate B time (sec)	Time from A to B (sec)	Speed at A (m/sec)	Speed at B (m/sec)	Acceleration (m/sec^2)

4 Thinking about what you observed

a. Calculate the speeds and acceleration of the car for each trial.

b. If there were no friction, what would the acceleration of the car be?

c. Use the second law to calculate for force of friction (in N) for each trial of the rolling cart.

d. Make a graph showing the force of friction on the vertical (y) axis and the mass of the cart on the horizontal (x) axis. Scale the graph so you can plot both sliding and rolling friction on the same graph.

e. Describe the relative strength of the friction forces for sliding and rolling.

f. How does the force of friction vary with mass? Is the variation the same for rolling and sliding friction?

g. How does the force of rolling friction vary with speed? Make a graph showing the force of friction at different average speeds for carts with the same mass.

Projectile Motion

Question for this Investigation:

How can you predict the distance a projectile will travel?

Toss a ball some distance and you can imagine in your mind the arc it follows, first rising then falling to the ground. The path the ball follows is the subject of this Investigation. Projectile motion describes objects moving under the influence of gravity, including thrown balls, coasting spacecraft, and even meteors.

Materials

- Marble launcher
- 8 m tape measure
- Room at least 3 m high and 7 m long.
- Graph paper
- Timer and photogate
- Safety goggles

Safety Tip: Wear safety goggles during the investigation.

The Marble Launcher

The range is the horizontal distance a projectile travels between launch and touch down. In this experiment you will see how the range depends on the launch angle.

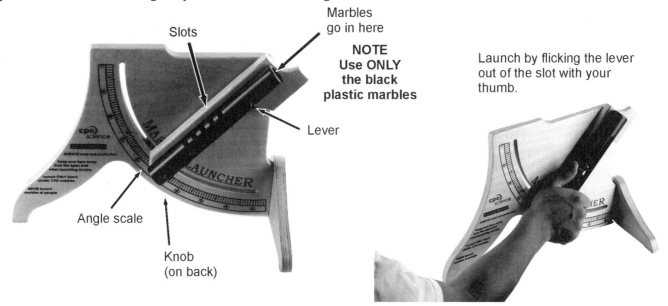

1. Set up by marking a tape line on the floor. This line is where you set the front edge of the launcher.
2. One person launches while several group members stand to either side to spot where the marble first touches the ground.
3. Place a marble in the barrel and then pull the pin back and slide it into one of the five slots.
4. Use your thumb to flick the pin out of the slot and launch the marble.
5. Use only the black plastic marbles, and follow all safety rules.
6. Spotting the landing point is tricky. It often takes several launches to figure out where the marble lands.

2 ▲ Variables and techniques

a. What two variables most affect the range of the marble? (Hint: Both are adjusted on the Marble Launcher)

b. If you wish to study the effect of changing one variable, what must be done with the other one?

c. Place a photogate on the end of the Marble Launcher so the marble breaks the light beam as it leaves the barrel. Connect the photogate to the timer. How can the photogate be used to ensure consistent results?

Photogate

3 ▲ Measuring range versus angle

1. Choose which release slot on the barrel of the marble launcher to use for all your range measurements.
2. Practice your technique until you can launch marbles with times that are within 0.0002 seconds of each other.
3. Measure the range every ten degrees from 10 to 90 degrees, and also at 45 degrees.

Table 1: Range versus angle data

Launch Angle (degrees)	Distance (meters)	Launch Angle (degrees)	Distance (meters)
10		50	
20		60	
30		70	
40		80	
45		90	

4 ▲ Thinking about what you observed

a. Make a graph with launch angle on the *x*-axis and range on the *y*-axis.

b. Use your graph to find the angle that launches the marble with the greatest range.

c. The Marble Launcher starts the marble more than 10 cm above the floor. Suppose the marble were launched from floor level. Do you think it would go a shorter, longer, or about the same distance? Explain why.

d. You are challenged to launch a marble to travel a distance of 3.00 meters. At what angle will you set the launcher?

e. Referring to your answer for question (c), state another angle that would give you the same result.

Motion on a Ramp

Question for this Investigation:

How does gravity work on a ramp?

This Investigation takes a closer look at motion on a ramp. Motion on a ramp is important in many ways. For example, highway engineers need to understand this kind of motion because hills that are too steep are dangerous. The angle of the ramp measures the steepness of the hill.

Materials

- Car and track
- Timer and photogates
- Physics stand

1 ◣ Acceleration on a ramp

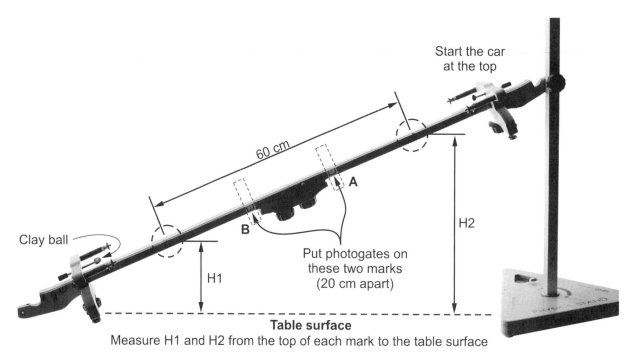

Measure H1 and H2 from the top of each mark to the table surface

1. Set up the two-section straight track with two photogates 20 cm apart near the center. Use a threaded knob to attach one end to the physics stand.

2. Attach one stop as high as you can to provide a repeatable start point for the car. Put a clay ball on the other stop at the bottom of the track.

3. Measure the height of the track in two places 60 cm apart, as shown in the diagram (H1 and H2).

4. Roll the car down and measure the three photogate times. This will allow you to calculate the acceleration from the difference in speed between photogates A and B.

5. Change the mass of the car and repeat the experiment. Use only two different masses for the entire experiment.

6. Change the angle and do the experiment for at least 6 different angles from nearly flat to nearly vertical. Test each angle with both masses for the car.

Table 1: Speed and height data

Mass (kg)	Height H1 (cm)	Height H2 (cm)	H2 - H1 (cm)	Length (L) (cm)	Time photogate A (sec)	Time photogate B (sec)	Time A to B (sec)

2 ⏵ Thinking about what you observed

a. The steepness of the hill is described by the ratio of height over length. What is this ratio for a ramp that is vertical (straight up)? What is the ratio for a ramp that is horizontal?

b. Calculate the ratio of (H2 - H1) ÷ L for the angles you tested. Record the results in Table 2, column 4 under "Steepness ratio."

c. Calculate the speeds and acceleration of the rolling car for each trial (Table 2, columns 1, 2, 3).

d. Make a graph showing the acceleration of the car on the vertical (y) axis and the steepness ratio on the horizontal (x) axis.

e. Research the acceleration of an object dropped straight down in free fall. How does this acceleration compare to the acceleration you determined on the ramp? How does the steepness ratio figure into the relationship between acceleration straight down and acceleration along the ramp?

Useful relationships

$$\text{Acceleration} = \frac{\text{Speed at B - Speed at A}}{\text{Time from A to B}}$$

$$\text{Speed} = \frac{0.01 \text{ m}}{\text{Time through photogate}}$$

---

f. Use Newton's second law to calculate the force acting on the car that causes it to accelerate on the ramp (Table 2, column 5).

g. How does the force in column 5 compare to the *weight* of the car? How does the steepness ratio figure into the relationship between weight and force along the ramp?

h. Research a mathematical name for the steepness ratio.

Table 2: Calculations

1 Speed at A (m/sec)	2 Speed at B (m/sec)	3 Acceleration (m/sec^2)	4 Steepness ratio (H2 - H1) / L	5 Force (N)

Temperature and Heat

Question for this Investigation:

1. How is temperature different from energy?

Hot and cold are familiar sensations but you may not have known that they are caused by the energy of atoms! This Investigation will explore the concept of temperature and also the difference between temperature and thermal energy (heat).

Materials

- Digital thermometer 0-100°C
- Mass balance
- Ten 1/2" steel washers
- Foam cups
- Ice
- Cold water
- Hot water

---

1 ◤ Thinking about temperature and energy

Consider the following experiment. Two foam cups contain equal masses of water. One cup contains cold water with a temperature of 0°C. The other contains hot water with a temperature of 50°C. The hot water is mixed with the cold water and stirred.

Measure 100 g of hot and cold water

Mix the hot and cold water together

What is the mixture temperature?

a. Which cup has more energy, the hot one or the cold one? Why do you think so?

b. What do you think the temperature of the mixture will be? Why?

c. If the system includes both the cold and hot water, compare the energy of the system before mixing to the energy after mixing. You may ignore any energy going to air or friction.

2 ◤ Doing the experiment

1. Prepare foam cups contain 100 g each of hot and cold water.
2. Measure and record the temperatures before mixing.
3. Mix the water, stir well, and measure the final temperature.

Table 1: Temperature data for mixing equal masses of water

Cold water temperature before mixing (°C)	Hot water temperature before mixing (°C)	Mixture temperature (°C)

Thinking about what you observed

a. Given the actual hot and cold temperatures, what do you think the mixture's temperature should be?

b. Did the result of the experiment agree with your prediction? Discuss the meaning of "agree" in terms of the accuracy and precision of your experiment.

 A more complex experiment

Assume you have 3 foam cups and each contains an equal mass of water. One cup contains cold water with a temperature of 0°C. The other two contain hot water with a temperature of 50°C. For this experiment assume T_1 to be 0°C for each cup. For this experiment, T_2 is the temperature of each cup of water before mixing. All three cups are mixed together and stirred. The final temperature of the mixture is T_f.

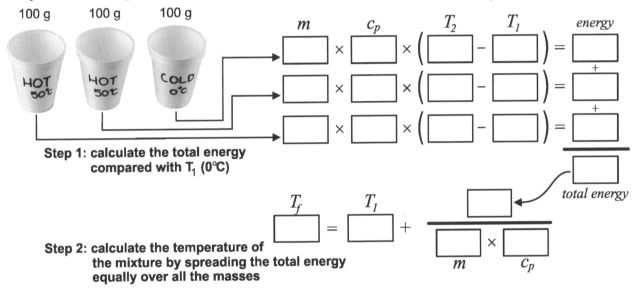

100 g 100 g 100 g

Step 1: calculate the total energy compared with T_1 (0°C)

Step 2: calculate the temperature of the mixture by spreading the total energy equally over all the masses

a. What do you think the temperature of the mixture will be? Why?

b. The thermal energy contained by the water in each cup is given by the formula $E = mc_p(T_2 - T_1)$. Write down what each of the symbols (m, c_p, T_2, T_1) means.

c. It takes 4,184 J of energy to raise the temperature of one kg of water by 1 °C. This quantity(C_p) is called the specific heat of water (4,184 J/kg°C). Use this information to calculate the mixture temperature by assuming the energy of the hot water is equally distributed in the final mixture. Follow the steps in the diagram above to predict the final temperature after mixing.

5 **Doing the experiment**

1. Prepare 3 foam cups, 2 containing 100 g each of hot water, and 1 containing 100 g of cold water.
2. Measure and record the actual temperatures before mixing.
3. Mix the water, stir well, and measure the final temperature.

Table 2: Temperature data for mixing equal masses of water

Cold water temperature before mixing (°C)	Hot water temperature before mixing (°C)	Mixture temperature (°C)

6 ▶ Doing an experiment with metal and water

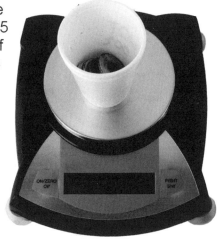

Measure 100 - 125 grams of washers (cold)

Add the same mass of hot water to the cold washers

WASHERS 0°C 105.48

What is the mixture temperature?

1. Put enough washers in a foam cup so the mass is between 150 and 200 grams. Record the mass of the washers.

2. Cover the washers with ice and water so they become cold.

3. Prepare an equal mass of hot water in another foam cup.

4. Record the temperature of the cold water and washers, then pour off all the water leaving just the washers in the cup.

5. Add the equal mass of hot water to the cup with the washers.

6. Mix the water, stir well, and measure the final temperature.

Table 3: Temperature data for combining water and steel washers

Washer Mass (kg)	Washer temperature before mixing (°C)	Hot water mass (kg)	Hot water temperature before mixing (°C)	Mixture temperature (°C)

7 ▶ Thinking about what you observed

a. Calculate the expected mixture temperature for the three cups of water in part 5. How does this compare with your actual mixture temperature? Suggest explanations for any differences.

b. Why didn't the temperature of the steel and water mixture come out halfway between cold and hot, even though you mixed equal masses?

c. Different materials have different abilities to store thermal energy. Research and describe the property of a material that measures its ability to store heat. What units does this property have?

d. How much energy does it take to raise the temperature of a kilogram of steel by 1 °C?

e. (Challenge problem) Suppose you drop 0.5 kg of steel at 100°C into a bucket containing 2 kg of water at 0°C. What is the final temperature of the mixture? (Hint: apply energy conservation)

Energy and Phase Changes

Question for this Investigation:

How is energy involved when matter changes phase?

We experience matter in three phases: solid, liquid, and gas. Changing from one phase to another means changing the bonds between atoms therefore energy must either be used or given off. This Investigation will explore how much energy it takes to change matter from one phase to the next.

Materials

- Digital thermometer 0-100°C
- Mass balance
- At least four foam cups
- Ice
- Cold water
- Hot water

 Doing the experiment

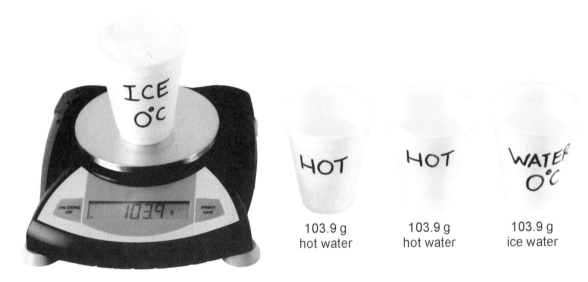

103.9 g
hot water

103.9 g
hot water

103.9 g
ice water

Measure equal masses into all four cups
(103.9 g is example only, use your own mass)

1. Place some crushed ice in cold water, then transfer at least 100 g of ice into a cup. Try not to get any liquid water, just ice.
2. Measure the mass of the ice and cup.
3. Prepare another cup with an equal mass of cold ice water (with ice removed).
4. Prepare two cups with an equal mass of hot water
5. Measure and record the temperatures before mixing. Assume the solid ice is at 0°C.
6. Mix the ice and hot water in one cup and the hot and cold water in another cup. Stir well, and measure the final temperature of each mixture after all the ice has melted.

Table 1: Temperature data for mixing equal masses of water

Liquid cold water plus hot water		
Cold water temperature before mixing (°C)	Hot water temperature before mixing (°C)	Mixture temperature (°C)
Solid water (ice) plus hot water		
Ice temperature before mixing (°C)	Hot water temperature before mixing (°C)	Mixture temperature (°C)
0		

2 ▲ Thinking about what you observed

a. Given the actual hot and cold temperatures, what do you think the mixture temperature should have been if the ice could change to liquid (of the same temperature) without any change in energy?

b. Was the final temperature of the mixture for the ice + water mixture about the same, more, or less than the final temperature of the water + water mixture?

c. Explain the difference in temperatures using the concepts of energy and phase change (heat of fusion). You may refer to the following diagram.

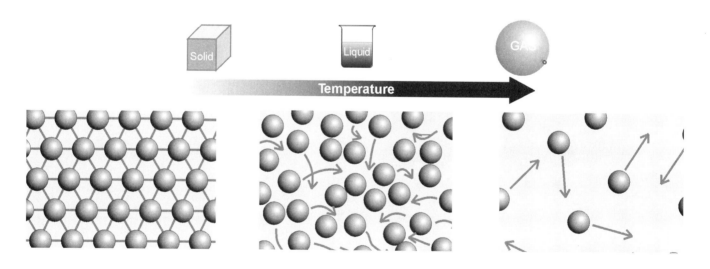

Density and the Phases of Matter

Question for this Investigation:

How do equal masses of gas, solid, and liquid compare?

Air is a gas and it has considerable mass. In this Investigation you will measure the amount of matter in a solid, a liquid, and a gas and compare the number of atoms per cubic meter (density).

Materials

- Mass balance
- 1-liter plastic soda bottle
- Prepared bottle cap with inserted tire valve
- Tire pressure gauge
- Bicycle pump
- Large graduated cylinder

The gas phase

Safety Note: Be careful with the bottle, and DO NOT exceed 70 pounds per square inch (psi) of pressure.

1. Get the prepared cap with the tire valve inside and a 1-liter carbonated soda bottle.
2. Fill the bottle to the very top with water. Empty the water into a graduated cylinder to measure the volume of the bottle.
3. Put the cap on the empty bottle (full of air) and measure the mass.
4. Use the bicycle pump to raise the pressure in the bottle to 10 psi. Check the pressure with your gauge.
5. Use the balance to measure and record the mass of the bottle (and air) at 10 psi pressure.
6. Repeat the pumping and mass measurement for pressures between 10 psi and 70 psi. DO NOT exceed 70 psi!

Table 1: Pressure and mass data

Gauge pressure (psi)	Mass (g)	Volume (ml)

Thinking about what you observed

a. What happens to the mass as you increase the pressure in the bottle?

b. Explain why your mass changed.

3 ⯈ Graphing the data

a. Use Table 2 to calculate the mass of air added to the bottle at different pressures.

Table 2: Calculating the mass of air

Pressure (psi)	Mass of bottle and air (g)	Mass of bottle at zero gauge pressure	Mass of air added to bottle (g)
		-	=
		-	=
		-	=
		-	=
		-	=
		-	=

b. Make a graph showing the mass of air plotted against the pressure.

c. When the pressure is zero on the gauge, is there any air in the bottle? Use the graph (or your data) to estimate the mass of air in the bottle at atmospheric pressure (zero on the gauge).

4 ⯈ Liquid and solid phases

1. Use your balance to measure out a quantity of water of equal mass to the air at zero gauge pressure.

2. Use your balance to measure out a quantity of solid material (coins, salt or sugar work well) of equal mass to the air at zero gauge pressure.

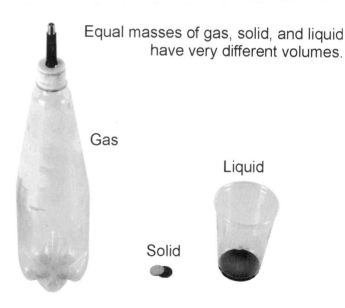

Equal masses of gas, solid, and liquid have very different volumes.

Gas

Liquid

Solid

5 ⯈ Thinking about what you observed

a. Compare the total amount of matter in the gas, liquid, and solid samples. Does one have more matter? Does one have less matter? Or, do all have about the same amount of matter?

b. Most of the mass in ordinary matter is in protons and neutrons. How does the total number of protons and neutrons compare in each of the three samples (solid, liquid, gas)?

c. How does the number of atoms compare in each of the three samples (solid, liquid, gas)? How can the number of atoms be different from the total number of protons and neutrons?

d. Compare the relative density of each of the three samples (solid, liquid, gas).

Motion of Fluids

Question for this Investigation:

How does pressure affect fluids?

Everything obeys the law of energy conservation. It just gets trickier when investigating a fluid (liquid or gas). You still have potential and kinetic energy, but you also have pressure energy. If friction is neglected, the total energy stays constant for any particular sample of fluid. This relationship is known as Bernoulli's principle.

Materials

- Bendable plastic straw
- Water
- 3 x 3" sticky note
- Plastic tub to catch water
- Cardboard milk or juice carton

1 Demonstrating Bernoulli's equation

For this experiment, you will need a plastic straw and a sticky note that is about 3-by-3 inches.

1. Cut a strip of the sticky note about 2 centimeters wide. Stick the note on a desk as shown at right.

2. With the straw, blow air across the sticky note from the stuck side toward the free side.

3. Observe what happens to the paper as the moving air blows across its upper surface.

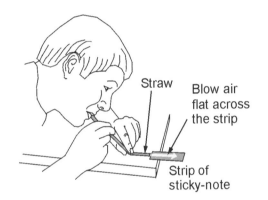

Straw

Blow air flat across the strip

Strip of sticky-note

2 Thinking about what you observed

a. Does the paper curl up into the moving air or down away from the moving air?

b. Force has units of mass multiplied by acceleration. Energy has units of force multiplied by distance. What are the units of pressure?

c. Show that the units of pressure are identical to the units of *energy density*. Energy density is energy divided by volume, or joules per cubic meter.

d. When you blow air what happens to its kinetic energy? Does the kinetic energy increase, decreases, or stay the same?

e. If the kinetic energy increases, the energy must come from somewhere. Where does it come from and how does this change the pressure?

f. Use the concept of pressure to explain why the paper lifts up when you blow air over it.

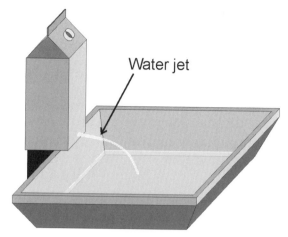

3 Demonstrating energy conservation

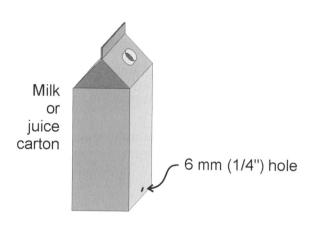

Milk
or
juice
carton

6 mm (1/4") hole

Water jet

1. Get a cardboard milk or juice container and poke a round hole about 6 mm (1/4") in diameter near the bottom.
2. Set the container above a pan to catch water.
3. Fill the container to the top with water and observe the jet of water coming out of the hole.

4 Thinking about what you observed

a. What happens to the speed of the water jet coming out of the hole as the carton empties out? Does the speed stay the same, get faster, or get slower as the water level goes down? How can you tell?

b. How does the pressure change with depth in a fluid?

c. Where does the kinetic energy of the moving water jet come from?

d. Use the law of energy conservation to explain the observed speed of the water jet as the carton empties out.

e. What would happen to the speed of the water jet if you blow into the carton and increase the pressure? Why do you think so? Try the experiment (if you can) and see if your prediction is correct.

5 Bernoulli's equation

The relationship between pressure, height, and speed in a fluid is given by Bernoulli's equation. Bernoulli's equation is a direct result of writing down energy conservation for a fluid. Many inventions rely on Bernoulli's equation, including airplane wings.

a. Research Bernoulli's equation and give a 2-3 sentence explanation of how a wing creates lift forces large enough to fly a plane. You may refer to the diagram on the right in your answer.

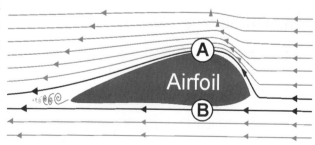

Airfoil

A

B

38

The Atom

Question for this Investigation:

How is an atom organized?

We once believed that atoms were the smallest units of matter. Then it was discovered that there are even smaller particles inside atoms! The structure of the atom is the underlying reason nearly all the properties of matter we experience are what they are. This Investigation will lead you through some challenging and fun games that illustrate how atoms are built from protons, neutrons, and electrons.

Materials

- Atom building game

1 Modeling an atom

In the atom game, colored marbles represent the three kinds of particles. Red marbles are protons, blue marbles are neutrons, and yellow marbles are electrons.

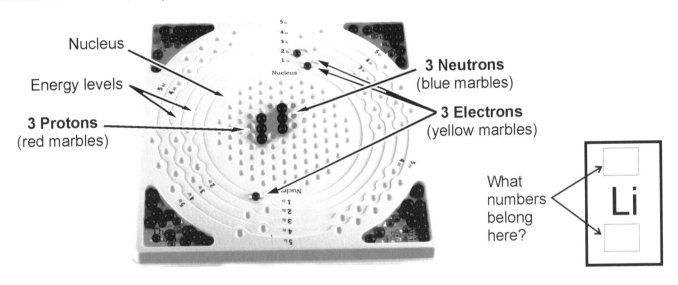

1. Build the atom above using three red, three blue, and three yellow marbles.
2. Fill in the blanks in the empty periodic table box for the atom you constructed.

2 Thinking about the atom

  a. What is the number below the element symbol called and what does this number tell you about the atom?

  b. What is the number(s) above the element symbol called and what does this number tell you about the atom?

  c. Why do some elements have more than one number above the symbol? What are the variations in this number called?

3 ◢ The Atomic Challenge

Atomic Challenge is a game that simulates the periodic table of elements.

The winner of the game is the first player to use all their marbles.

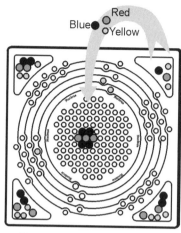

1. Each player should start with the following marbles: 6 blue marbles (neutrons), 5 red marbles (protons), and 5 yellow marbles (electrons).

2. Each player takes turns adding 1 - 5 marbles, but not more than 5. The marbles may include any mixture of electrons, protons, and neutrons.

3. Marbles played in a turn are added to the marbles already in the atom.

4. If you add marbles that make an atom NOT shown on the periodic table you have to take your marbles back and lose your turn. Only atoms where the electrons, protons, and neutrons match one of the naturally occurring elements on the table are allowed.

$$Li^7 + p + n + e = Be^9$$

5. A player can trade marbles with the bank INSTEAD of taking a turn. The player can take as many marbles, and of as many colors as they need but must take at least as many total marbles as they put in. For example, a player can trade 2 yellows for 1 yellow, 1 blue, and 1 red.

The Three Rules

Rule #1: The number of protons matches the atomic number

Rule #2: The total number of protons and neutrons equals a stable mass number

Rule #3: The number of electrons matches the number of protons

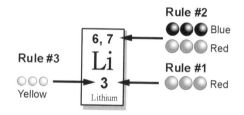

4 ◢ Using the periodic table

Atoms which are not on the periodic table shown (see next page) may exist in nature but they are radioactive and unstable. For example, carbon-14 (C^{14}) is unstable and is not listed although C^{12} and C^{13} are stable.

a. How many electrons does an atom of neon (Ne) have?

b. How many stable isotopes does oxygen (O) have?

c. Find one element on the periodic table that has no stable isotopes.

d. What element has atoms with 26 protons in the nucleus?

e. On most periodic tables a single atomic mass is listed instead of the mass numbers for all the stable isotopes. How is this mass related to the different isotopes?

Periodic Table of the Elements 1- 54
(Stable isotopes)

Key

Element Symbol — Mo
Atomic Number — 42
Stable Mass Numbers — 92, 94-100

1,2 H 1																	3,4 He 2
6,7 Li 3	9 Be 4											10,11 B 5	12,13 C 6	14,15 N 7	16-18 O 8	19 F 9	20-22 Ne 10
23 Na 11	24-26 Mg 12											27 Al 13	28-30 Si 14	31 P 15	32-34, 36 S 16	35,37 Cl 17	36,38, 40 Ar 18
39,41 K 19	40,42-44,46, 48 Ca 20	45 Sc 21	46-50 Ti 22	51 V 23	50, 52-54 Cr 24	55 Mn 25	54,56-58 Fe 26	59 Co 27	58,60-62,64 Ni 28	63,65 Cu 29	64,66-68,70 Zn 30	69,71 Ga 31	70,72-74,76 Ge 32	75 As 33	74,76-78,80,82 Se 34	79,81 Br 35	78,80,82-84,86 Kr 36
85 Rb 37	84,86-88 Sr 38	89 Y 39	90-92,94,96 Zr 40	93 Nb 41	92,94-100 Mo 42	none Tc 43	96,98-103,104 Ru 44	103 Rh 45	102,104-106,108,110 Pd 46	107,109 Ag 47	106,108,110-112,114,116 Cd 48	113 In 49	112,114-120,122,124 Sn 50	121 Sb 51	120,122,124-126,128,130 Te 52	127 I 53	124,126,128-132,134,136 Xe 54

Energy and the Quantum Theory

Question for this Investigation:

How do atoms absorb and emit light energy?

The electrons in an atom are organized into energy levels. You can think of energy levels like a staircase where the electrons can be on one step or another but cannot exist in-between steps. When an electron changes levels, the atom absorbs or emits energy, often in the form of light. This Investigation will teach you a challenging and fun game that simulates how atoms exchange energy through light. The process is fundamentally how a laser works.

Materials

* Atom Game

The neon atom

1. Build a neon atom with 10 each of protons (red marbles), neutrons (blue marbles) and electrons (yellow marbles).

2. Set the electrons in the lowest spaces possible.

3. Find the following cards in the Photons and Lasers can
   Pump 1 (red)
   Pump 2 (yellow)
   Laser 1 (red)

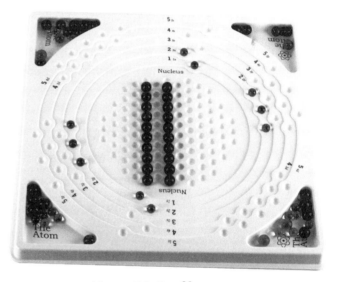

Neon-20 (Ne^{20})

10 protons, 10 neutrons, 10 electrons

How atoms exchange energy

a. Explain the meaning of the term "ground state" when applied to an atom.

b. Can the second energy level of neon hold any more electrons? How does this affect neon's chemical properties and position on the periodic table?

c. Take the red "pump 1" card from your hand and put it on the atom board. Move one electron from level 2 to level 3. Explain what this sequence of actions represents in a real atom.

d. Take the yellow "pump 2" card from your hand and put it on the atom board. Move any one electron up 2 levels. Explain what this sequence of actions represents in a real atom.

e. Take the red "laser 1" card from your hand and put it on the atom board. Move any one electron down one level. Explain what this sequence of actions represents in a real atom.

The photons and lasers game 3

Photons and
lasers
card deck

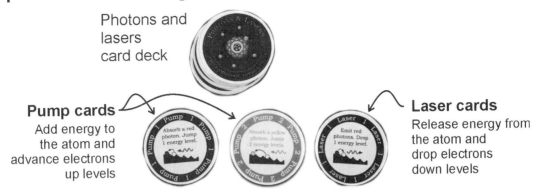

Pump cards — Add energy to the atom and advance electrons up levels

Laser cards — Release energy from the atom and drop electrons down levels

1. The first player to reach 10 points wins the game.

2. Each player starts with 5 cards and plays one per turn, and then draw a new card to maintain a hand of 5.

3. Playing a pump card allows the player to advance one electron up by the number of levels shown on the card (1 - 4). No points are scored by playing pump cards.

4. Playing a laser card allows the player to drop electrons from one level to a lower level. The player scores one point per electron per level. For example, moving 2 electrons down 2 levels scores 4 points.

5. Rules for playing laser cards:
   Electrons can only be moved down if there are empty states for then to move to.
   Electrons can only be moved from one level in a turn.
   If the card says "laser 2" then each electron must move 2 levels.

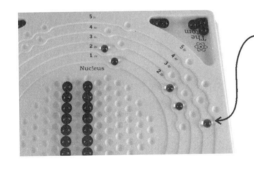

A **Laser-2** card can drop this electron 2 levels scoring 2 points

4 **Thinking about what you learned**

a. What does the term "excited state" mean with respect to energy and atoms?

b. What physical principle prevents two electrons from moving into the same state?

c. In order of increasing energy, arrange the following colors of light: blue, red, green, yellow.

d. Could an atom emit one photon of blue light after absorbing only one photon of red light? Explain why or why not.

e. Suppose a real atom had energy levels just like the game. Could this atom make blue-green light with an energy in between blue and green? Explain what colors this atom could make.

   Take the spectrometer and look at the light from a fluorescent lamp. It looks white but you will see lines of certain colors. The lines are proof that electrons in atoms really do have energy levels.

Energy and Efficiency

Question for this Investigation:

How well is energy transformed from one form to another?

According Newton's laws you could start a car moving in a frictionless world and it would continue with the same speed forever. The real world is never frictionless however, so the car slows down. In fact, all real processes that exchange energy dribble away small amounts to friction and heat. This Investigation is about efficiency which describes how well energy is transformed in a process.

Materials

- Energy car and track
- Timer and photogates
- Meter stick

 Kinetic energy exchange

1. Set up the long straight track so it is level with rubber bands on both ends.
2. Position a photogate so the flag breaks the light beam just before hitting the rubber band.
3. Use the one rubber band to send the car bouncing off the rubber band near the photogate.
4. Measure the time through the photogate before and after the car hits the rubber band. You will need to use the memory button to display the "before" time. Catch the car after the bounce.
5. Record at least two trials with consistent data and calculate the average speeds before and after hitting the rubber bands.
6. Measure the mass of the car and do the experiment for several different masses.

Table 1: Kinetic energy data

Mass of the car (kg)	Time before collision (sec)	Speed before collision (m/sec)	Time after collision (sec)	Speed after collision (m/sec)

2 **Thinking about what you observed**

a. Describe the energy flows that occur between the car heading toward the rubber band and the car leaving the rubber band.

b. If the transformation of energy were perfect (100% efficiency) what would you expect the speed of the car to be before and after the collision with the rubber band?

c. Write down the formula for kinetic energy and use the formula to calculate the kinetic energy of the car before and after bouncing off the rubber band.

Useful relationships

Kinetic energy $= \frac{1}{2} mv^2$

Efficiency $= \dfrac{\text{Final energy}}{\text{Initial energy}}$

d. Calculate the efficiency of the process of bouncing the car off a rubber band.

 3 **How does the efficiency change?**

1. Adjust the deflection of the rubber band to get different speeds for the car. Bounce the car off the other rubber band at different speeds and record the photogate data.

Table 2: Energy efficiency data

Mass of the car (kg)	Time before collision (sec)	Speed before collision (m/sec)	Time after collision (sec)	Speed after collision (m/sec)

4 **Thinking about what you observed**

a. Calculate the efficiency of the rubber band for the different masses and speeds you tested.

b. Plot a graph showing the efficiency on the vertical (*y*) axis and the speed on the horizontal (*x*) axis. How does the efficiency change with the speed of the car?

c. Try changing the tension of the rubber band. Does this effect the efficiency?

5 **How long does it take for the energy to be gone?**

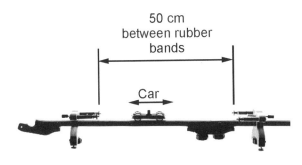

50 cm between rubber bands

Car

Suppose the car is allowed to bounce back and forth between two stops that are 50 cm apart. Assume the car starts with the maximum kinetic energy it can get from the rubber band. Estimate how many bounces the car can complete before coming to a stop.

1. Move the stops so they are about 60 cm apart. Keep the track level.

2. Launch the car and count how many bounces it makes before coming to rest.

45

Energy Flow in a System

Question for this Investigation:

How does the energy move through a series of transformations?

Most systems in the world exchange energy in may forms as they operate. To understand how things work we often trace the flow of energy. The performance of a machine can be improved by working at improving each step where energy is used. This Investigation traces the energy in a three step process using the car.

Materials

- Energy car and track
- Physics stand
- 0 - 2.5-N force scale
- Meter stick

1 ⮞ Tracing the energy through the system

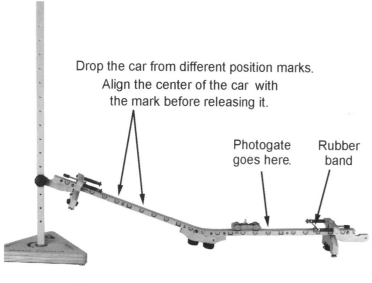

Drop the car from different position marks. Align the center of the car with the mark before releasing it.

Photogate goes here.

Rubber band

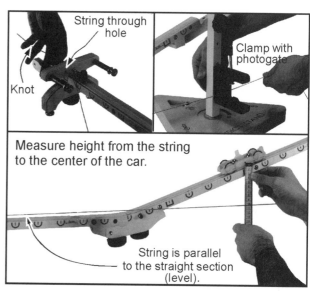

String through hole

Knot

Clamp with photogate

Measure height from the string to the center of the car.

String is parallel to the straight section (level).

1. Set up the track with a hill and a level section.
2. Put a photogate in the center of the level section.
3. Use the photogate to measure the speed of the car before and after it bounces off the rubber band.
4. Drop the car from different heights to get several different speeds.
5. Measure the mass of the car. Do the experiment for several different masses.

Table 1: Energy data

Drop Height (m)	Mass of car (kg)	Time before rubber band (sec)	Speed before rubber band (m/sec)	Time after rubber band (sec)	Speed after rubber band (m/sec)

Thinking about what you observed

a. What three forms of energy are most important to the motion of the car in this system?

b. Calculate the total energy of the car in joules at three places:
(1) At the top of the hill before it is dropped,
(2) At the photogate heading into the rubber band for the first time,
(3) At the photogate after bouncing off the rubber band.

c. Describe the three most important energy transformations that occur during the motion (other than friction).

d. Draw an energy flow diagram showing the measured and calculated amounts of energy at each of the three measured places. Label any energy that is lost as "friction."

Example energy flow diagram

Energy form 1

90%   10%

Energy form 2

80%   20%

Energy form 3   Friction

e. What percentage of its initial energy does the car have after passing through the photogate for the second time? Assume the car has "lost" any energy spent overcoming friction.

f. Where does the energy "lost" to friction go? Is the energy really destroyed?

Improving the overall performance

a. Suggest a modification you can make to the system that would leave the car with a higher percentage of energy after the second pass through the photogate.

b. Explain why you believe your modification will result in higher energy efficiency.

c. Write down a few sentences describing a procedure to test your modification.

Testing your idea

a. Design an experiment that will test your idea for improving overall energy efficiency. Write down a procedure for doing the experiment. Write down what data you expect to record and how the data will allow you to evaluate your idea.

b. Set up and do the experiment you designed.

c. Analyze the results from your experiment. Compare the percentage of energy the car has after the second pass through the photogate to what it was in the earlier experiments. Your answer must use data from your experiment.

d. Give at least one reason why the efficiency is higher, lower, or about the same compared to what it was in the experiment.

Energy and Chemical Changes

11A

Question for this Investigation:

How do chemical changes involve energy?

Atoms come together in molecules by making _chemical bonds_ with other atoms. Chemical bonds are a form of energy. When atoms change their bonds in a _chemical reaction_, energy can be either used or given off. In this Investigation, you will make chemical reactions and deduce whether they use energy or give off energy.

Materials

- Timer in stopwatch mode
- 10 grams of ammonium nitrate
- 5 grams of sodium hydrogen carbonate (baking soda)
- Safety goggles
- Electronic balance

- Thermometer
- Graduated cylinder
- 10 grams of calcium chloride
- Safety apron

- 3 250-mL beakers
- 100 mL vinegar
- 200 mL distilled water
- Graph paper
- Paper towels

1. Reaction #1: Ammonium nitrate and water

In this reaction, you will observe the temperature while adding about 10 grams of ammonium nitrate to 100 mL of distilled water.

Measure 10 g of ammonium nitrate.

Measure 100 mL of water into a 250 mL beaker.

Add the ammonium nitrate to the water and stir gently with the thermometer.

1. Put 100 mL of distilled water in a clean 250-mL beaker.
2. Measure the initial temperature of the water and record it in Table 1.
3. Keeping the thermometer in the water, add 10 grams of ammonium nitrate and stir gently with the thermometer.
4. Measure the temperature every 10 seconds for a total of 90 seconds and record your date in Table 1.

Table 1: Time and temperature data for ammonium nitrate and water

Record the temperature(°C) for each time (sec)									
0	10	20	30	40	50	60	70	80	90

2 ▸ Thinking about what you observed

a. Did the temperature go up, down, or stay the same when you did the experiment?

b. Why does a change in temperature indicate a change in energy?

3 ▸ Reaction #2: Calcium chloride and water

For this reaction, you will add about 10 grams of calcium chloride to 100 mL of distilled water.

Measure 10 g of
calcium chloride

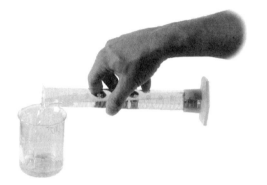

Measure 100 mL of
water into a 250 mL beaker

Add the calcium chloride
to the water and stir gently
with the thermometer

1. Put 100 mL of distilled water in a clean 250-mL beaker.
2. Measure the initial temperature of the water and record it in Table 1.
3. Keeping the thermometer in the water, add the 10 grams of calcium chloride and stir gently with the thermometer.
4. Measure the temperature every 10 seconds for a total of 90 seconds and record your date in Table 2.

Table 2: Time and temperature data for calcium chloride and water

Record the temperature(°C) for each time (sec)									
0	10	20	30	40	50	60	70	80	90

4 Reaction #3: Vinegar and baking soda

Add 5 grams of baking soda (sodium hydrogen carbonate) to 50 mL of vinegar (acetic acid solution).

Measure 5 grams
of baking soda

Add to 50 mL of vinegar and
stir gently with the thermometer

1. Put 50 mL of vinegar in a clean 250 mL beaker.
2. Measure the initial temperature of the vinegar and record it in Table 1.
3. Keeping the thermometer in the liquid, add the 5 grams of baking soda.
4. Measure the temperature every 10 seconds for a total of 90 seconds and record your date in Table 3.

Table 3: Time and temperature data for vinegar and baking soda

Record the temperature(°C) for each time (sec)									
0	10	20	30	40	50	60	70	80	90

5 Thinking about what you observed

a. A reaction that gives off energy is called _exothermic_. Which reaction(s) are exothermic? Support your answer with data.

b. A reaction that uses energy is called _endothermic_. Which reaction(s) are endothermic? Support your answer with data.

c. Graph time vs. temperature for each reaction on the same graph. Use a different color pen for each reaction.

d. What does the graph show about energy changes in each reaction? Describe what is happening in each reaction based on the graph.

e. Cold packs can be purchased at your local pharmacy and are used to treat injuries. Which reaction is most likely the one used in cold packs? Explain your answer.

f. One of the solids you used in the reactions can be purchased at a hardware store and is used to melt snow and ice in winter. Which chemical is it? Explain your answer.

Nuclear Reactions and Radioactivity

Question for this Investigation:

How do nuclear changes involve energy?

You would be very surprised to see a bus spontaneously transform into three cars and a motorcycle. But radioactive atoms do something very similar. If left alone, a radioactive atom eventually turns into another kind of atom, with completely different properties. This Investigation looks at some basic concepts behind radioactivity.

Materials

- Atom building game
- 50 pennies
- Cup
- Graph paper

1 ▶ Radioactivity

Heads

Tails

Set 50 pennies heads up on the desk

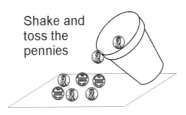

Shake and toss the pennies

Pennies that land heads-up go back in the cup for the next toss

Pennies that land tails-up are put aside

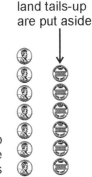

1. Place 50 pennies in a paper cup, shake them and dump them on the table. Each penny represents an atom of carbon-14.
2. Separate the pennies that land tails-up. Count the heads-up pennies and tails-up pennies and record the number of each in Table 1 in the row for the first toss.
3. Put *only the pennies that landed heads-up* back in the cup. Put the tails-up pennies aside. Shake the cup again and dump the pennies on the table.
4. Record the number of heads-up pennies in the row for the second toss.
5. Repeat the experiment using only the pennies that landed heads-up until you have one or no pennies left.

Table 1: Coin toss decay simulation

	Heads-up pennies	Tails-up pennies
Start	50	0
First toss		
Second toss		
Third toss		

 Thinking about what you observed

a. Make a graph showing the number of heads-up pennies on the *y*-axis and the number of tosses on the *x*-axis (0, 1, 2, 3,...).

b. On average, what percentage of pennies are lost on each toss? "Lost" means they came up tails and were removed.

c. How does the concept of half-life relate to the experiment with pennies? What does one half-life correspond to?

 Build a radioactive atom

Carbon - 14

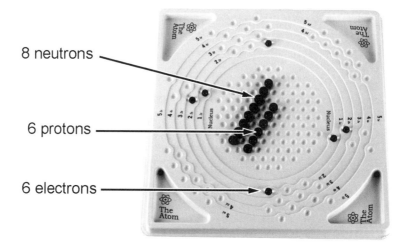

8 neutrons
6 protons
6 electrons

1. Build a carbon-14 atom (C^{14}). This isotope of carbon is radioactive.
2. Take one neutron out and replace it with a proton and an electron. This is what happens in radioactive decay of C^{14}.

 Thinking about what you did

a. Research what happens to C^{14} when it decays. What element does it become? What particles are given off?

b. What is the average time it takes for 50% of the C^{14} atoms in a sample to decay?

c. Suppose you have 50 atoms of C^{14} and you watch them for a very long time. How do the results of your penny-flipping experiment describe the number of C^{14} atoms?

d. We actually find C^{14} in the environment. Research where it comes from.

e. Describe two other types of radioactivity and give an example of each.

f. (Challenge) You cannot predict when any one atom will decay, just as you cannot predict whether a penny will come up heads or tails. Why can you predict that 50% of the C^{14} atoms will decay every half-life?

Frames of Reference

Question for this Investigation:

How does your frame of reference affect what you observe?

The word "relativity" refers to the idea that what you experience depends on the relative motion of your frame of reference. This Investigation is about frames of reference and it will give you a window into the meaning of relativity.

Materials

- Car and track
- Timer and photogates
- An AV car or table with wheels

Demonstrating two frames of reference

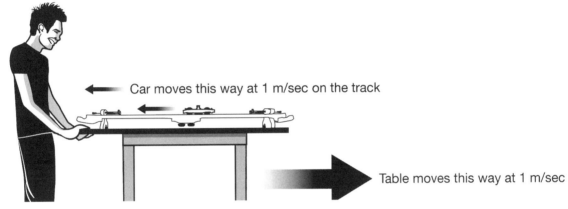

Car moves this way at 1 m/sec on the track

Table moves this way at 1 m/sec

1. Put the 2 sections of the straight track together and make it level on the rolling table.

2. Adjust the launcher to propel the car at an approximately constant speed of 1 m/sec.

3. Mark a distance of 3 - 4 meters on the floor with tape.

4. Use the stopwatch mode of the timer to calibrate your pace so you can push the rolling table in the opposite direction of the car at a constant speed of 1 m/sec. Don't worry about getting things exact, it is only a demonstration of an idea.

5. The person pushing the rolling table should look only at the car on the track. The rest of the group should stand to the side and watch the car from their perspective.

This person watches only the car on the track on the table.

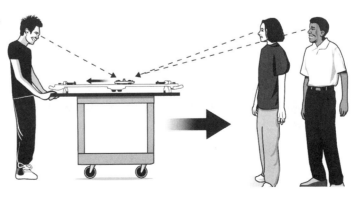

These people watch the car relative to the classroom and do not look at the table.

2 Thinking about what you observed

a. Imagine the person pushing the table was in a box, able only to see the car and track and nothing outside the box. What motion of the car do they see relative to themselves?

b. What motion of the car do the outside observers see relative to themselves?

c. There are two important frames of reference in this demonstration. What are they?

d. One frame of reference is in motion relative to the other. What is this motion?

e. Suppose the table was rolling at exactly 1 m/sec relative to the room and the car was rolling in the same direction at 1 m/sec relative to the track. What is the speed of the car relative to the room? How do you arrive at this answer?

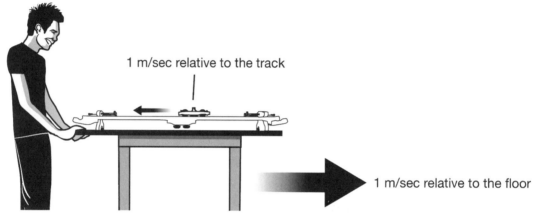

1 m/sec relative to the track

1 m/sec relative to the floor

3 A thought experiment

Imagine you are watching a train from a distance. You see two bolts of lightning hit the train at the same time. To you, the two events (lightning strikes) are *simultaneous* because it takes the same amount of time for light from either event to reach you.

If you were sitting on the train however, it is a different situation. Suppose you are in the center of the train. If the train were at rest, you would see two simultaneous lightning strikes. But, the train is moving. The train moves between the time the lightning hits and when light from the lightning reaches you.

Whether two events occur at the same time depends on the relative motion of your frame of reference

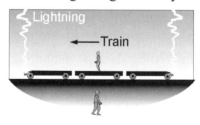

a. When you are on the moving train, do you observe the lightning hit the front of the train first, the back first, or does light from both lightning strikes reach you at the exact same time?

b. (Discussion question) Explain the reasoning behind your answer of question (a) above.

According to Einstein, two events happen at the same time (for you) if the light from each reaches you at the same time. This is a different meaning for "at the same time." This is a clue that *time itself* is dependent on your frame of reference. Many people find this idea very strange, but it is true. Time passes at different rates in reference frames that are moving relative to each other.

Relativity

Question for this Investigation:

What is the theory of relativity about?

Newton's laws work very well for ordinary motions. However, when things *really* get moving Newton's laws no longer give the right answer. Einstein's theory of relativity describes how Newton's laws are modified at speeds close to the speed of light. The word "relativity" refers to the idea that what you experience depends on the relative motion of your frame of reference. Observers whose frames of reference are moving relative to each other do not always see the same things.

Materials

- None, this is a "thought and discussion" Investigation

1 An imaginary experiment with light - Special relativity

With ordinary speeds, the speed *you* measure depends on the relative motion of *your* frame of reference. The fundamental rule of the theory of relativity is that the speed of light is always the same *even if your frame of reference is moving*. This single idea caused Einstein to change all our concepts of space and time.

Einstein imagined having a clock that measures time by counting the trips of a beam of light going up and down between two mirrors. The clock is on a moving spaceship. A person standing next to the clock sees the light go back and forth straight up and down. The time it takes to make one trip is the distance between the mirrors divided by the speed of light.

Special relativity says the speed of light is the same for every observer, regardless of relative motion.

A light clock counts trips of light between two mirrors

Tick   Tock   Tick   Tock

In the ship the light goes straight up and down

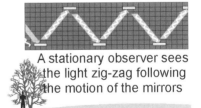

A stationary observer sees the light zig-zag following the motion of the mirrors

To someone who is not moving, the path of the light is not straight up and down. The light appears to make a zigzag because the mirrors move with the spaceship.

This would not be a problem, except that the speed of light must be the same to all observers, regardless of their motion. How can this be?

Thinking about what you imagined

The following are all questions for class discussion. They are challenging!

a. Describe the two reference frames that are important. Who is in each one?

b. What is the relative motion between the two reference frames?

c. Does the person on the ground see the light travel a distance that is longer, shorter, or the same compared to the distance seen by the person watching the light on the space ship?

d. Prior to Einstein, speed was always calculated as the distance traveled divided by the time taken. Thinking this way, does the person on the ground see the light in the clock move faster, slower, or at the same speed compared to what the person in the space ship sees.

e. The theory of relativity requires that the speed of light be the same for all observers, regardless of relative motion. If the speed is the same, but the distance is different, what other variable must also be different in the two reference frames?

f. Do clocks on board the space ship run slower, faster, or at the same rate compared to clocks on the ground?

 General relativity

a. Suppose "straight line" is defined as "the path of motion an object follows when the net force acting on it is zero." Does this definition describe the same thing as your previous mathematical definition of a "straight line"?

Path of a ball on
a flat surface

Path of a ball on
a warped surface

View from overhead

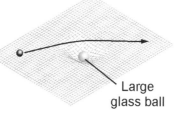
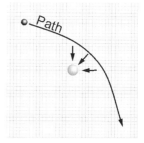

Large
glass ball

b. Suppose you stretch a rubber sheet and place a heavy glass ball in the center. The glass ball depresses the sheet a few centimeters. A plastic ball is rolled in a straight line from the edge of the sheet as shown in the diagram. Sketch the path of the plastic ball as it passes by the glass ball.

c. Suppose the rubber sheet was completely transparent, and you could not see the glass ball either. Propose an explanation that would explain the observed path of the plastic ball using the idea of force.

 Einstein's two theories

Einstein's special theory of relativity (1905) describes how space and time change when objects move at speeds near the speed of light. Einstein's general theory of relativity (1915) describes how objects with mass distort the very shape of space itself. What we describe as gravitational force is really due to the curvature of space caused by mass.

Electricity

Question for this Investigation:

How is electricity measured and described?

We use electricity every day, almost every minute. In this Investigation you will build circuits and learn about voltage (volts) and current (amps) which are fundamental quantities that describe the electricity we use.

Materials

- Electric circuits kit
- 2 "D" batteries
- Digital multimeter with test leads
- Pieces of foil, wood, plastic, metal paper clips, and other small objects.

Building a circuit

Single bulb circuit

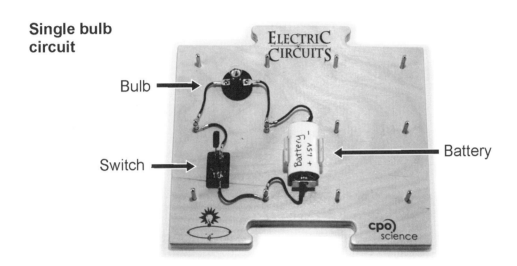

Bulb

Switch

Battery

1. Build the circuit shown in the diagram with one battery, a switch, and a bulb.
2. Open and close the switch and see what happens.

Thinking about what you observed

a. How can you tell electric current is flowing in the circuit? Can you see the current flow?

b. Current flows from positive to negative. Trace the flow of current around the circuit with your finger.

c. How does the switch cause the current to stop flowing?

d. Why does the bulb go out when you open the switch?

e. Draw an energy flow diagram of the circuit. Label the forms of energy that appear.

3 ▸ Conductors and insulators

Materials in which electric current flows easily are called _conductors_.
Materials that current does not flow through easily are called _insulators_.

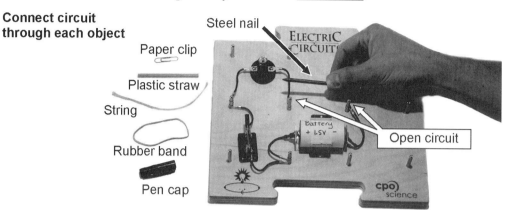

1. Break one connection in your one-bulb circuit.
2. Complete the circuit by touching different materials between the wire and the post.
3. Which materials allow the bulb to light and which do not?

4 ▸ Thinking about what you observed

a. Make a table listing the materials as either conductors or insulators.

b. What characteristics are shared by the conductors you found?

c. What characteristics are shared by the insulators you found?

5 ▸ Measuring the voltage of a battery

Turn the dial of your multimeter to DC volts. Red goes to the positive terminal and black to the negative terminal. Touch two points in a circuit with the leads and the meter reads the voltage between the two points.

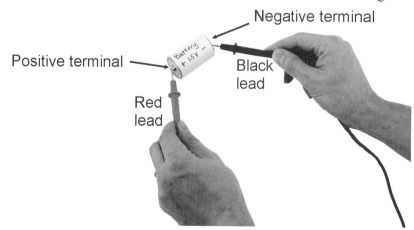

1. Measure the voltage of the battery and record your reading.
2. Take a second battery and connect it to the first by touching the ends together.
3. Measure the voltage for the four possible ways to connect two batteries (+ to -, + to +, - to -, - to +). How do your readings compare to the voltage of just one battery?

6 Measuring current

To measure current, the meter must be connected so the current has to flow through it.
This is different from voltage measurement. To measure current you must force the current to flow through the meter by eliminating all other paths the current could go. Follow the instructions below carefully. Too much current can damage the meter.

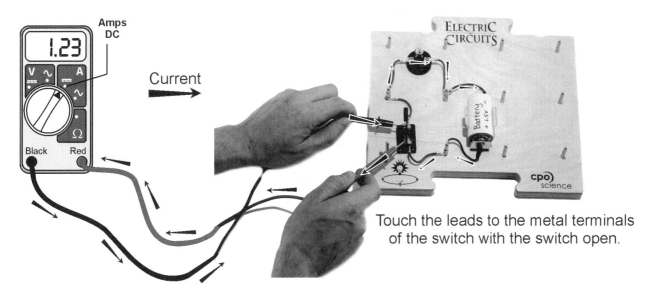

Touch the leads to the metal terminals
of the switch with the switch open.

1. Set the multimeter to measure DC amps (current).
2. Open the switch and touch the red lead of the meter to the metal part of the switch closest to the battery's positive terminal (+).
3. Touch the black lead of the meter to the metal part on the other side of the switch.
4. The bulb should light, showing you that current is flowing through the meter. The meter should display the current in amps. This is the total current flowing around the circuit carrying power from the battery to the bulb. Remove the meter.

a. How much current is flowing in the circuit when the bulb is making light?

7 Circuit diagrams

For describing electric circuits we use the language of *circuit diagrams*. In a circuit diagram wires are represented by solid lines. Electrical devices like switches, batteries, and bulbs are represented by symbols.

a. Using these symbols, draw a picture of the circuit you built with one battery, switch, and light bulb.

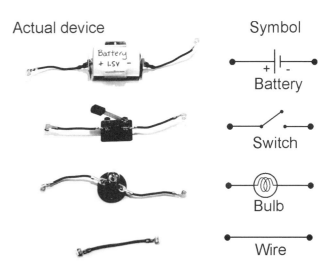

Actual device   Symbol

Battery

Switch

Bulb

Wire

8 ◢ A circuit with a dimmer switch

The potentiometer (or *pot*) is an electrical device that can be used to make a dimmer switch. When the dial on the pot is turned one way the pot acts like a closed switch and current flows freely through it. When the dial is turned the pot resists the flow of current depending on the position of the dial.

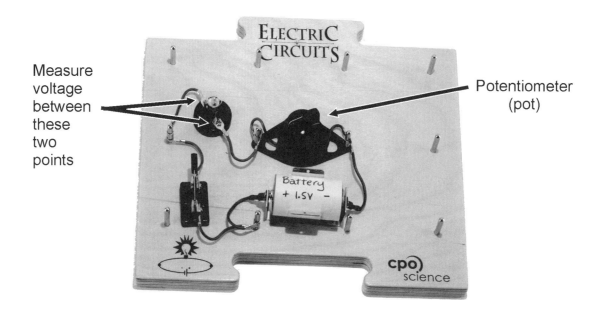

1. Connect the circuit in the diagram using the pot, a battery, wire, and a bulb.
2. Adjust the dial and watch what happens to the bulb.
3. Use the meter to measure the voltage across the bulb for different settings of the pot. Record your data in table 1.

Table I: Pot settings and voltage across bulb

Pot dial position	Voltage across bulb (V)	Observed light output of bulb

9 ◢ Thinking about what you observed

a. As you changed the settings of the pot, what happened to the voltage across the bulb?

b. Did you observe a relationship between the voltage across the bulb and the light output?

c. Propose a relationship between power and voltage that would explain the light output of the bulb.

Resistance and Ohm's Law

Question for this Investigation:

What is the relationship between current and voltage in a circuit?

Electrical devices use energy. They get the energy from the current that flows through them. When designing an electrical device, or a circuit, it is important for the proper amount of current to flow for the voltage that will be applied. This Investigation looks at resistance, which is the property that relates current and voltage in a circuit or electrical device.

Materials

- Electric circuits kit
- 2 "D" batteries
- Digital multimeter with test leads
- Pieces of foil, wood, plastic, metal paper clips, and other small objects.

 Measuring resistance

Resistance is measured in ohms (Ω). If a device has a resistance of 1 ohm (1 Ω), then a voltage of 1 volt will cause a current of 1 amp to flow. Your meter has a setting that allows it to measure the resistance of objects.

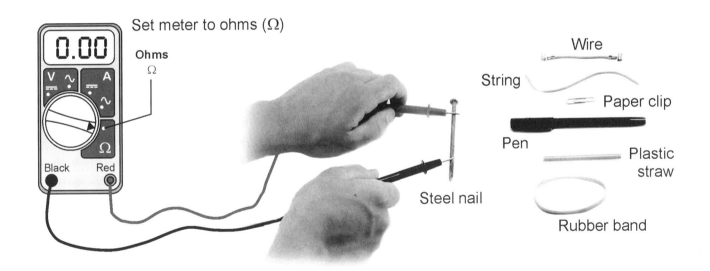

1. Set the multimeter to measure resistance.
2. Attach the two leads and test the various items that you previously identified as insulators or conductors in Investigation 13A. Record their resistance in Table 1.

Table 1: Resistance Measurements

Object description	Conductor or Insulator	Resistance (Ω)

2 ▸ The meaning of resistance

a. What relationship did you notice between the resistance and whether a material was a conductor or insulator?

b. Describe the ability of an object to conduct electrical current in terms of its resistance.

c. Write down Ohm's law and describe what each of the three symbols stands for (including units).

d. Two simple circuits are built with two different electrical devices. Each contains the same size battery. One device has a resistance of 100 ohms (100 Ω) and the other has a resistance of 1,000 ohms (1,000 Ω or 1 kΩ). Which circuit has more current? Use the concept of resistance to explain why.

3 ▸ Mystery resistors

A *resistor* is used in a circuit to provide resistance. You have resistors in your kit with values of 5 Ω, 10 Ω and 20 Ω but you don't know which is which!

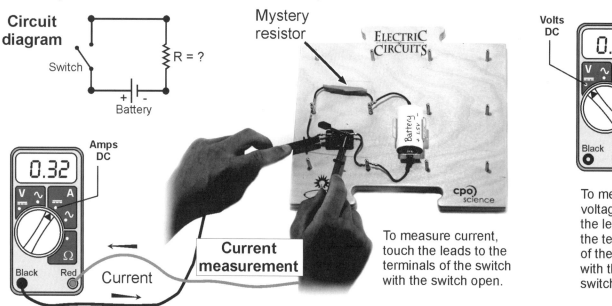

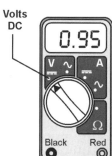

1. Make a circuit with a switch, battery, and resistor. Leave the switch open.
2. Measure the battery voltage.
3. Set the meter to measure current (DC amps). Open the switch. Measure the current by connecting the meter across the open terminals of the switch.
4. Repeat the test for each of the three different colored resistors.

Table 2: Resistor Currents

Resistor color	Battery voltage (V)	Current (amps)

a. Use your knowledge of Ohm's law to determine which resistor is which. The resistance you calculate from Ohm's law will not come out exactly to 5, 10, or 20 because the meter itself has a small resistance.

4 Resistance and potentiometers (pots)

The potentiometer (pot) you used in Investigation 13A is really a *variable resistor*. A variable resistor allows you to change its resistance by turning a dial. Many dials you use every day, like dimmer switches, are actually potentiometers.

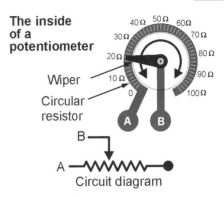

1. Use the meter to measure the resistance of the pot for different positions of the dial.

2. Take your first reading with the pot turned all the way to the left and take 4 or 5 readings until the pot is turned all the way to the right.

Table 3: Pot settings and resistance

Pot dial position	Resistance (Ω)

5 The bulb dimmer circuit

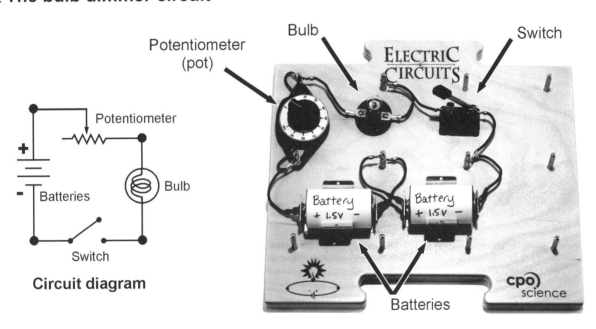

Circuit diagram

1. Build the dimmer circuit with two batteries, the pot, a switch, and a bulb.

2. Close the switch and observe how the brightness changes as you change the dial on the pot.

a. Use the concept of resistance to explain how the pot controls the brightness of a bulb.

b. Suppose the resistance of the bulb is 5Ω. The total resistance of the circuit is 5Ω plus the resistance of the pot. Use Ohm's law to calculate the maximum and minimum current flowing through the circuit when the pot is turned fully on or off. Assume a voltage of 3.0 V is applied by the battery.

6 The voltage drop

The voltage in a circuit is reduced whenever current flows through a device that has a resistance greater than zero. The reduction of voltage is called the *voltage drop*. The voltage drop is described by Ohm's law.

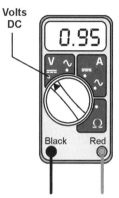

Volts DC

To measure the voltage drop across the pot, touch the leads to (A) and (B).

Use points (B) and (C) to measure the voltage drop across the bulb.

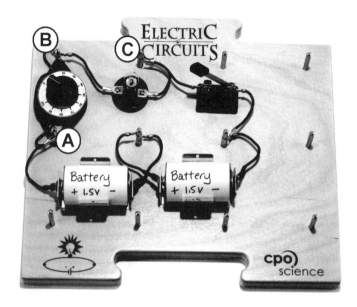

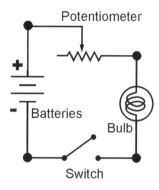

Circuit diagram

1. Connect the dimmer circuit with the pot, switch, two batteries, and a light bulb.
2. The voltage drop is measured by touching the meter leads to the terminals of each device.
3. Measure the voltage drop across the pot and across the bulb for different dial settings of the pot.

Table 4: Pot settings and voltage drops

Pot dial position	Voltage drop across pot (V)	Voltage drop across bulb (V)	Observed light output

a. What relationship do you observe between the voltage drop across the pot and the voltage drop across the bulb?

b. What does the voltage drop tell you about the electrical energy carried by the current?

c. What relationship do you observe between the measured voltage drops and the battery voltage?

Electric Circuits

Questions for this Investigation:

What are the different types of circuits?

A simple electric circuit contains one electrical device, a battery, and a switch. Flashlights use this type of circuit. However, most electrical systems, such as a stereo, contain many electrical devices connected together in multiple circuits. This Investigation introduces two ways to connect multiple devices in a circuit.

Materials

- Electric circuits kit
- Digital multimeter with test leads
- 2 "D" batteries

 Series circuits

Build this circuit

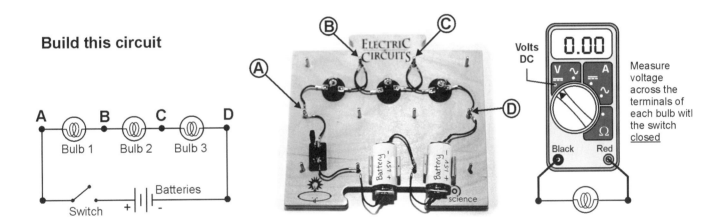

1. Using two batteries, build the simple circuit with three light bulbs and a switch as shown above.
2. Set the meter to DC volts. Close the switch and measure the voltage across the different places by touching the meter's leads to the bulbs' terminals. Record the voltages in Table 1.

Table 1: Voltage measurements (volts)

Between A and B	Between B and C	Between C and D	Between A and D

 Thinking about what you measured

a. What relationships do you see among the voltage measurements in Table 1?

b. What do the voltage measurements tell you about the flow of energy in the circuit?

3 The current in series circuits

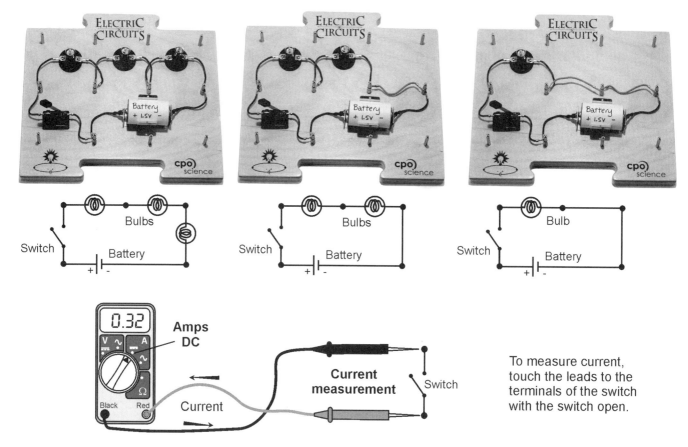

To measure current, touch the leads to the terminals of the switch with the switch open.

1. Set the meter to DC amps. Measure the current by opening the switch and touching the leads of the meter to the terminals of the switch in the three bulb circuit. Record your measurements in Table 2.

2. Remove one bulb and replace it with a wire. Measure and record the current for the two-bulb circuit.

3. Remove a second bulb and replace it with a wire. Measure and record the current again for the one-bulb circuit.

Table 2: Current Measurements (amps)

Three bulbs	Two bulbs	One bulb

4 Thinking about what you observed

a. What happens to the current in the circuit as the number of bulbs is reduced? Explain why this occurs using Ohm's law and the concept of resistance.

b. What happens to the other two bulbs when one bulb is removed from the three-bulb circuit? Try it and explain why the circuit behaves as it does.

5 ⟩ Short circuits

A short circuit is an easy (but dangerous) shortcut that current can travel through to avoid one or more of the electrical components in the circuit.

Circuit diagram

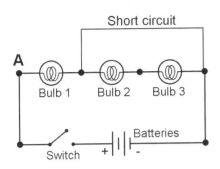

1. Rebuild your three-bulb circuit with the switch open.
2. Check the current and observe which bulbs light and how bright they are.
3. Add a section of wire that bridges the last two bulbs in the circuit. This wire is the "short circuit."
4. Complete the circuit (with the switch open) using the meter to measure the current. Observe which bulbs light and how bright they are.

6 ⟩ Thinking about what you observed

Table 3: Short Circuit Current Measurements (amps)

Three bulbs in series	Three bulbs with two short circuited

a. Compare the current in the three-bulb circuit with the current when two bulbs are bypassed by a short circuit. Which is greater? Use Ohm's law and the concept of resistance to explain why.

b. How does the current in the "short circuit" version compare with the current you measured in a one-bulb circuit? Explain why this should be true.

c. How does the resistance of a wire compare to the resistance of a bulb? Measure the resistances to test your answer. NOTE: Most meters cannot measure very low resistance and display "0.00" when the resistance is lower than 0.01 Ω.

d. Why would a short circuit be dangerous? Discuss (as a class) the consequences of very large currents in wires of different sizes.

7 ► Parallel circuits

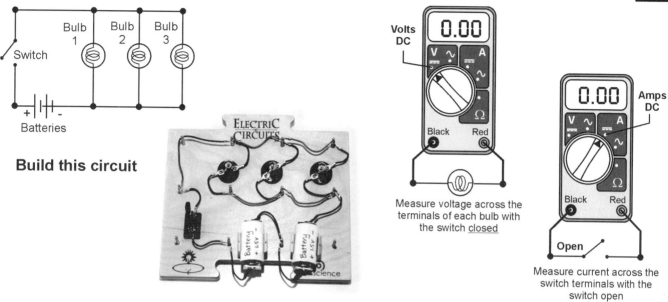

Build this circuit

Measure voltage across the terminals of each bulb with the switch <u>closed</u>

Measure current across the switch terminals with the switch open

1. Build a circuit with two batteries, a switch, and three bulbs as shown in the diagram.

2. Close the switch and measure the voltage across the battery. All three bulbs should be lit.

3. Measure the voltage across each bulb by touching the leads of the meter to the terminals of each bulb separately.

4. Set the meter to DC amps. Measure the total current in the circuit by opening the switch and touching the leads of the meter to the terminals of the switch.

Table 4: Voltage and current in a parallel circuit

	Total circuit	Bulb 1	Bulb 2	Bulb 3
Voltage (*V*)				
Current (*A*)				

8 ► Thinking about what you observed

a. Compare the brightness of the bulbs in the parallel circuit with the brightness in the series circuit.

b. Compare the total current in the single-bulb circuit, the three-bulb series circuit, and the three-bulb parallel circuit. Propose a relationship between the currents that agrees with the brightness of the bulbs.

c. Remove one bulb from the circuit by unscrewing it from its socket. Observe what happens to the remaining bulbs.

d. Did the other two bulbs continue to light when the third bulb was removed from the parallel circuit? Explain why. How does this differ from what happened with the series circuit?

e. Do you think the electrical outlets in your home are connected in a series or parallel circuit? Give two reasons why one type of circuit has an advantage over the other for connecting outlets.

Electrical Energy and Power

Questions for this Investigation:

How much energy is carried by electricity?

Materials

- Electric circuits kit
- Timer
- Digital multimeter with test leads
- 2 "D" batteries

1. Energy and power in an electrical system

A voltage of one volt means one amp of current can do one joule of work per second. This definition of a volt is really a formula for calculating power from current and voltage. If the voltage and current in a circuit are multiplied together, the result is the power used by the circuit.

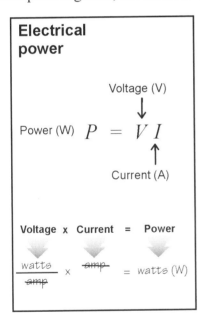

Electrical power

Voltage (V)

Power (W) $P = V I$

Current (A)

Voltage x Current = Power

$$\frac{watts}{amp} \times amp = watts \ (W)$$

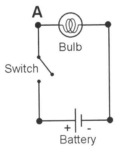

Circuit diagram

A
Bulb
Switch
+ −
Battery

1. Connect a simple circuit with a single bulb, switch, and battery.
2. Use the meter to measure the voltage and current in the circuit when the bulb is lit.
3. Use the formula above to calculate the power used by the bulb in watts.
4. Repeat the experiment with two batteries connected so the bulb receives 3 V instead of 1.5 V.

Table 1: Power used by a bulb

Voltage (V)	Current (A)	Power (W)

2 Thinking about what you observed

a. How did the power used by the bulb compare at the two different voltages?

b. Was the bulb brighter, dimmer, or about the same at 3 V compared to 1.5 V? Explain any difference you observed using the concept of power.

3 Energy and power from a battery

Circuit diagram

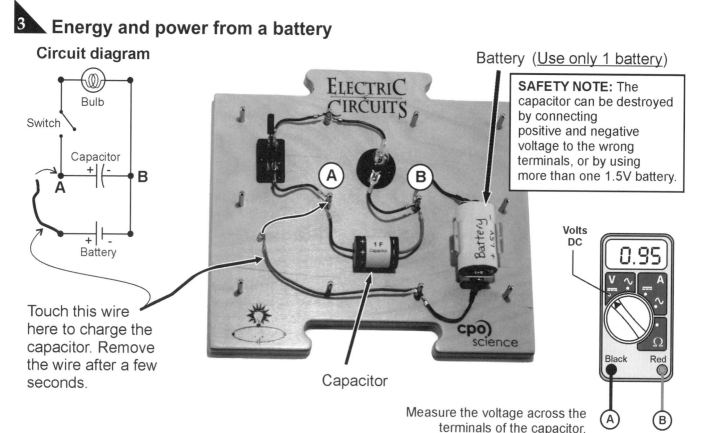

Battery (<u>Use only 1 battery</u>)

SAFETY NOTE: The capacitor can be destroyed by connecting positive and negative voltage to the wrong terminals, or by using more than one 1.5V battery.

Touch this wire here to charge the capacitor. Remove the wire after a few seconds.

Capacitor

Volts DC

0.95

Black   Red

Measure the voltage across the terminals of the capacitor. (A) (B)

1. Find the capacitor in the circuit set. This capacitor acts like a battery that charges almost instantly when you touch its terminals to a battery.

2. Make the circuit in the diagram. The positive terminal of the capacitor should meet the red (+) lead of the meter. The meter will probably read zero volts.

3. Touch the positive wire from the battery to the positive (+) terminal of the capacitor for 5 seconds. Remove the positive battery wire once the capacitor is "charged" up to 1.5 V.

4. Touch the wires from a bulb across the terminals of the capacitor while you watch the voltage of the capacitor with the meter. The bulb should light up then dim and go out as the voltage drops.

4 Thinking about what you observed

a. How was energy flowing when the capacitor was "charging up"? What was the source of the energy and where did it go?

b. How was energy flowing when the bulb was connected and the battery was removed? What was the source of the energy and where did it go?

c. Why did the bulb go out after a few seconds? Explain what you observed in terms of the ideas of energy and power.

5 ◢ Energy and power

You are going to use the Timer to measure how long the capacitor can keep one or more bulbs lit.

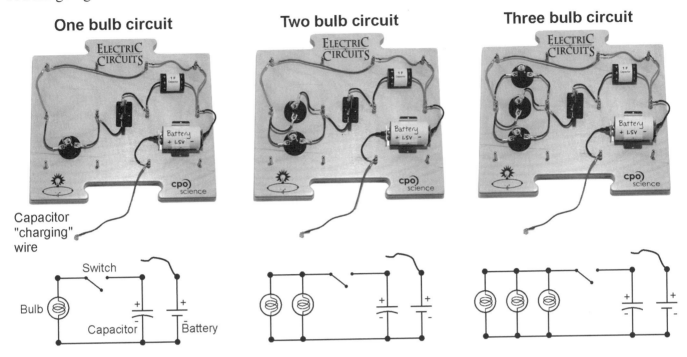

One bulb circuit   **Two bulb circuit**   **Three bulb circuit**

Capacitor "charging" wire

Switch

Bulb

Capacitor   Battery

1. Set up the three circuits above, one at a time.

2. For each circuit, charge the capacitor then use the Timer to measure how long the bulb produces light. Start the Timer when you close the switch to light the bulb. Stop the Timer when you can no longer see any light. Use stopwatch mode.

3. Repeat the test three times and take the average. Use Table 2 to record your data.

Table 2: Energy and power data at 1.5 V

Starting voltage (V)	Number of bulbs	Time until bulb goes out (sec.)			Average of 3 trials (sec.)

6 ◢ Thinking about what you observed

a. What is the total power used by 1, 2, and 3 bulbs connected in parallel? In a parallel circuit each device draws current as if it were the only device in the circuit.

b. What relationship do you observe between the time the bulbs stay lit and the total power used?

c. Since power is energy ÷ time, the formula can be rearranged to give energy = power × time. For example, if you use 10 watts for 10 seconds, you have used a total of 100 joules of energy (100 J = 10 W × 10 sec.). Use your data to estimate how many joules of energy are stored in the capacitor at 1.5 V.

Electric Charge

Questions for this Investigation:

What is "static" electricity?

We know that electric current is caused by the movement of tiny charged particles that break away from atoms and are free to move. Is it possible to see these tiny particles in any way? This Investigation looks at static electricity, which is caused by a small imbalance of electric charge.

Materials

- Clean glass bowl or cup
- Plastic rod
- Scissors
- Aluminum foil
- Fur and fleece fabric
- Thread
- 18 - 22 gauge copper wire
- Balloons
- Small nail

 Observing electric charge

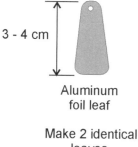

3 - 4 cm

Aluminum foil leaf

Make 2 identical leaves.

Use a small nail to drill the holes into the leaf by holding it against a foam cup.

Hang the leaf on some thread

Rub a balloon against your hair and bring it near the leaf.

1. Cut out some small "leaves" of aluminum foil and use a nail to drill a hole in the top of each leaf.
2. Suspend one leaf from a thread that you hold up in one hand.
3. Rub an inflated balloon against your hair and move it towards the foil leaf.
4. Touch the rubbed part of the balloon to something metal then bring it close to the leaf.
5. Bring other objects near the leaf before and after they are rubbed with different materials such as silk, fleece, or fur.

 Thinking about what you observed

a. Describe what happens to the aluminum foil leaf as you move the balloon closer.

b. Explain the reaction of the leaf to the rubbed balloon using the concepts of positive and negative charge.

c. Explain why touching the balloon to a metal object changed its effect on the leaf.

3 Making an electroscope

Aluminum
foil leaves
(2)

3 - 4 cm

Hang leaves on a
shallow hook
so they are free
to swing.

Wire

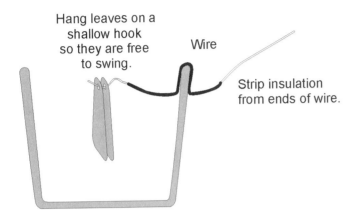

Strip insulation
from ends of wire.

Glass cup or bowl

Bring different charged and uncharged
objects near the wire.

1. Make the electroscope as shown in the diagram by hanging two leaves on the wire.
2. Rub an inflated balloon against your hair and move it towards the end of the wire sticking out of the bowl.
3. Touch the balloon to the wire then remove it.
4. Touch the end of the wire with your finger or a metal object.
5. Bring the plastic rod near the wire. Then rub the plastic rod with the fleece and bring it near the wire again.

4 Thinking about what you observed

a. Describe what happens to the aluminum foil leaves as you move the rubbed balloon closer.

b. Give a reason why the leaves stay apart after the balloon is removed.

c. Explain what happens when you touch the wire with your hand or a metal object.

d. "Charge" the electroscope by touching it with a balloon that has been rubbed against your hair. Then touch the rubbed side of the balloon to something metal and bring it close to the electroscope again. Describe what happens.

e. Why does the plastic rod cause the leaves to move only after it has been rubbed with the fleece?

f. What causes the leaves of the electroscope to move apart?

The Flow of Electric Charge

Question for this Investigation:

How many electrons move when current flows?

One electron is a very tiny amount of charge. The flow of current represents many, many electrons moving together. However, compared to the number of electrons that are in a material, the number that actually move and carry current is quite small. This Investigation will lead you inside the submicroscopic world of the atom to deduce how many electrons really move when one amp of current is flowing.

Materials

- Electric circuits kit
- Multimeter with red and black leads
- 1 "D" battery

Current and charge

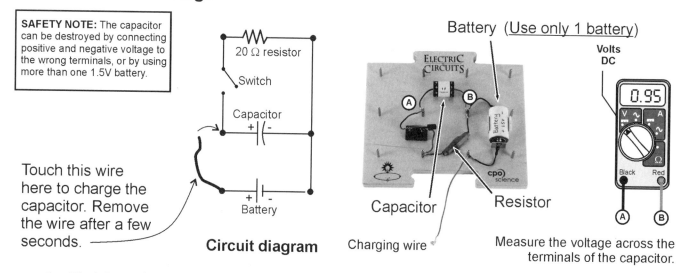

SAFETY NOTE: The capacitor can be destroyed by connecting positive and negative voltage to the wrong terminals, or by using more than one 1.5V battery.

20 Ω resistor

Switch

Capacitor
+ | | -

Battery
+ | | -

Touch this wire here to charge the capacitor. Remove the wire after a few seconds.

Circuit diagram

Battery (Use only 1 battery)

ELECTRIC CIRCUITS

Capacitor

Resistor

Charging wire

Volts DC

0.95

Black   Red

A   B

Measure the voltage across the terminals of the capacitor.

1. Find the resistor with a resistance of 20Ω.
2. Connect the circuit shown using the battery, capacitor, resistor, and switch.
3. Attach the meter to measure the voltage across the resister.
4. Charge the capacitor by touching the positive wire from the battery to the positive (red) lead of the capacitor. Count 5 seconds and then remove the positive battery wire.
5. Close the switch and record the voltage every ten seconds in Table 1.

Table 1: Capacitor discharge data

Time (sec)	Voltage (V)		Time (sec)	Voltage (V)
0			30	
10			40	
20			50	

2 ► How much current flowed?

a. Use Ohm's law to write down a formula for the current flowing through an electrical device if you know the voltage drop and the resistance.

b. Use the relationship you found in 2a (above) to fill in Table 2 by calculating how much current was flowing through the resistor.

Table 2: Capacitor current data

Time (sec)	Current (A)	Time (sec)	Current (A)
0		30	
10		40	
20		50	

3 ► Thinking about what you observed

a. Make a graph of the current versus time for the capacitor. Break the graph up into vertical bars that are ten seconds wide (See example graph below).

b. Set the height of each bar to the average value of the current over each ten second time interval. You can do this by eye since that will be good enough for the accuracy of the experiment.

c. Write down a formula that allows you to calculate the charge if you know the current and the time.

d. Calculate how much charge flowed in each ten second interval by multiplying the average current by ten seconds (Table 3).

e. Add up the charge from each interval to get the total charge. This is the amount of charge that was in the capacitor when it was "full."

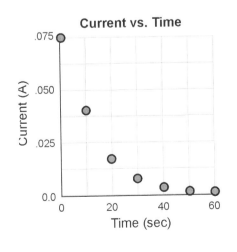

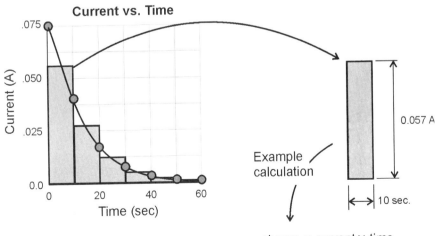

charge = current × time
= (0.057 A) × (10 sec)
= 0.57 C

Table 3: Calculating the charge

Average current (A)		Time Interval (sec)		Charge (C)
	X	10	=	
	X	10	=	
	X	10	=	
	X	10	=	
	X	10	=	
	X	10	=	
		Total for 60 seconds		

Estimating the number of electrons that move

a. Look up the charge of a single electron in coulombs (C).

b. Calculate how many electrons are in the total charge from Table 3.

c. Measure the mass of the capacitor in kilograms.

d. Estimate how many electrons are in the capacitor. You can do this calculation in the following steps:
(1) Write down the mass of a proton (1 amu) in kg.
(2) Calculate how many protons there are by assuming $\frac{1}{2}$ the mass of the capacitor is protons.
(3) The number of electrons is the same as the number of protons.

e. Calculate the number of electrons that move by dividing the result of step b by the number you found in step d.

Thinking about what you observed

a. Was the number of electrons that moved larger, smaller, or about the same as the number of electrons in the capacitor? Was the difference very large or very small?

b. Why were we able to estimate the number of protons as $\frac{1}{2}$ the total mass even though we did not know what elements the capacitor was made of?

c. Is the estimate of the number of electrons larger or smaller than the true number? Do you think the difference is larger or smaller than 25%? Give a reason for your answer.

Magnetism

Questions for this Investigation:

1. What are the effects of magnetism?
2. What kinds of materials are effected by magnetic force?

Magnets are used in almost all electrical and electronic machines from motors to computers and are able to exert strong forces at a distance. This Investigation will explore the properties of permanent magnets.

Materials

- Magnets
- Wood block
- Metric ruler
- Steel object
- Compass
- Plastic object

 How far does magnetic force reach?

How far does the magnetic force of a magnet reach? This is an important question concerning machines such as motors and generators that use magnets.

**How far does the
magnetic force reach?**

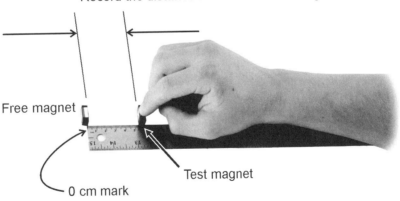

Record the distance at which the free magnet first moves.

Free magnet

Test magnet

0 cm mark

1. Place one magnet at the 0 cm mark of the ruler and slide a second magnet closer and closer until the first magnet moves. Practice the technique several times before recording data.
2. Record the distance between the magnets when you first see movement.
3. Try each of the combinations of poles—north-north, south-south, and north-south.
4. For each combination, complete three trials, and average your three distances.

Table 1: Magnetic forces between two magnets

	North-South	South-South	North-North
Distance 1 (mm)			
Distance 2 (mm)			
Distance 3 (mm)			
Average distance (mm)			

 Thinking about what you observed

a. When referring to many measurements of the same quantity, *precision* describes how close the measurements are to each other. Estimate the precision (in millimeters).

b. Look at your results and compare the average distances for the three combinations of poles. Are the attract and repel distances *significantly* different? In science, "significantly" means the differences are large compared to the precision of your measurement.

 Using a compass to detect magnetic forces

The needle of a compass is a permanent magnet. Because planet Earth is magnetic a compass needle is attracted to north in the absence of other (stronger) magnets. Because a compass can respond to the very small magnetism of Earth, a compass is a sensitive probe of magnetic forces.

Start:
Align the ring, arrow, and needle with north.

Measure the distance
to deflect the needle
20 degrees East.

Measure the distance
to deflect the needle
20 degrees West.

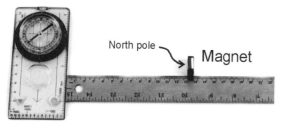

North pole — Magnet

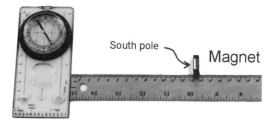

South pole — Magnet

1. Set a compass on your table far from any magnets. Rotate the compass so the needle, dial, and arrow are all aligned with north.

2. Place a metric ruler to the side of the compass and line it up perpendicularly with the north pole of the compass. Move a small magnet near the compass and record the distance at which the needle moves 20 degrees from north.

3. Reverse the pole of the small magnet and record the distance at which the needle moves 20 degrees in the opposite direction.

Thinking about what you observed

a. At a distance of 10 cm, which is stronger: the magnetic force from Earth or the magnetic force from the small magnet? How is your answer supported by your observations?

b. Is the end of the compass needle a magnetic north or a magnetic south pole? How is your answer supported by your observations?

c. Is the geographic north pole of the planet Earth a magnetic north or a magnetic south pole? How is your answer supported by your observations?

5 **Magnetic materials**

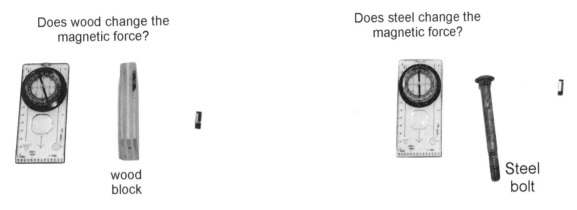

Does wood change the magnetic force?

wood block

Does steel change the magnetic force?

Steel bolt

1. Set the compass to north again with no magnets nearby.
2. Adjust the distance of a magnet until the deflection of the compass needle is 20 degrees east and record this distance in Table 2.
3. Place an object between the magnet and the compass.
4. If the deflection changes, adjust the distance of the magnet until the deflection returns to 20 degrees.
5. Record the interaction distance for five or six different materials, including plastic, wood, paper, and at least one iron or steel object that blocks an area the size of a business card or larger.

Table 2: Testing materials for magnetic effects

Material	20 degree deflection distance with air in between	20 degree deflection distance with material in between	Difference in distance	Percent difference

 Thinking about what you observed

a. Which materials made almost no change in the magnetic force? Can you list any common characteristics of these materials?

b. Which materials made a significant change in the magnetic force? Can you list any common characteristics of these materials?

Electromagnets

Question for this Investigation:

Can magnetic force be created?

Almost every electrical device that creates motion, such as a motor, uses magnets. However, some (or all) of the magnets are electromagnets. Electromagnets create magnetic forces through electric currents. This Investigation will explore some the properties of electromagnets.

Materials

- Magnets
- Electric circuits kit
- Steel nail, #16 or #20 size
- Metric ruler
- Electromagnet coil
- Sandpaper or wire stripper
- Compass
- Insulated wire, 22 gauge works well
- Plastic, wood, steel, and paper test objects

 Making an electromagnet

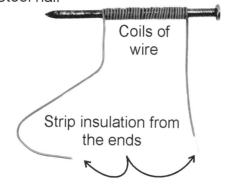

Steel nail

Coils of wire

Strip insulation from the ends

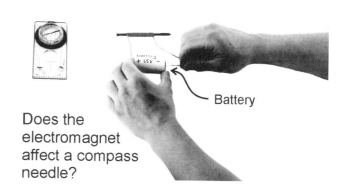

Does the electromagnet affect a compass needle?

Battery

1. Take about 60 centimeters of wire and wrap 30 turns around the nail.
2. Strip the insulation from the last centimeter of each end of the wire.
3. Set up a compass to detect the magnetic force from the electromagnet. Put the electromagnet about 15 cm from the compass.
4. Touch the wires briefly to a battery and watch the compass needle. DO NOT keep the electromagnet connected for more than a moment at a time because the wires will get hot.
5. Try reversing the connections to the battery so current flows the other way around the coil of wire.

 Thinking about what you observed

a. Does the compass needle move? What does this tell you about the force created by the electromagnet?

b. What happens when the current in the coil is reversed? Use your observations to support your answer.

c. Try wrapping 30 more turns on the coil. Does the magnetic force get stronger, weaker, or stay about the same? How do your observations support your answer?

3 Comparing the electromagnet to a permanent magnet

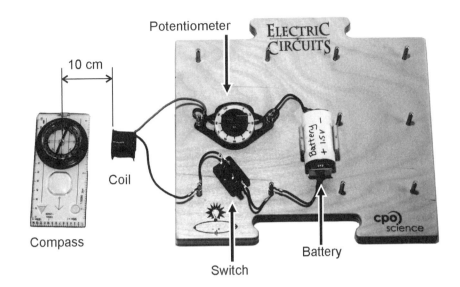

Potentiometer

10 cm

Permanent magnet

Adjust the distance of the permanent magnet so the compass needle is deflected 20 degrees away from north with the coil switched off (no current).

Coil

Compass

Switch

Battery

1. Attach the potentiometer, coil, battery, and switch in the circuit shown in the diagram. Leave the switch open so no current flows.

2. Set the compass so the needle, ring, and arrow are all aligned with north. Put the coil about 10 cm from the center of the compass.

3. Place a permanent magnet on the side of the compass opposite the coil. Bring the magnet close enough to deflect the needle 20 degrees away from north.

4. Close the switch and adjust the potentiometer so the needle returns to north. The coil should deflect the compass needle back toward north. Reverse the permanent magnet if the needle moves the wrong way. DON'T leave current running or the coil will overheat. Open the switch after each trial.

5. Try moving the permanent magnet to different distances and using the potentiometer to return the compass needle to north with force from the electromagnet.

4 Magnetic properties of materials

1. The permanent magnet is pulling the compass needle to the left. The electromagnet is pulling the needle in the opposite direction to the right. When the needle returns to north what can you say about the magnetic forces from the permanent magnet and electromagnet?

2. Put objects between the electromagnet and the compass and note whether the deflection changes. Use different materials, including plastic, wood, paper, and at least one iron or steel object

5 Thinking about what you observed

a. Based on your observations, propose a relationship between the current in the coil and the magnetic force produced. You may use the meter to measure the current to verify your hypothesis.

b. Which materials made almost no change in the magnetic force from the electromagnet? Can you list any common characteristics of these materials?

c. Which materials made a significant change in the magnetic force? Can you list any common characteristics of these materials?

81

6 Iron and electromagnets

Trial # 1: Coil only

Permanent
magnet

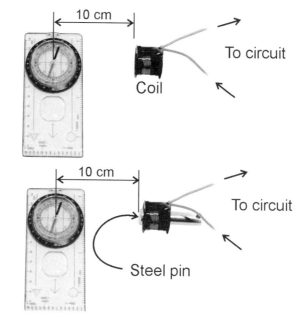

Measure the
current it takes
to bring the
compass needle
back to north

Trial # 2: Coil and steel pin

Permanent
magnet

1. Use the same circuit as for part 3 with one battery, switch, coil and potentiometer.

2. Rotate the compass until the needle and dial are aligned with north. *There should be no magnets nearby, and no current in the coil for this step.*

3. Move a permanent magnet close enough to deflect the needle 20 degrees from north.

4. Close the switch to measure and record how much current it takes for the coil to bring the needle back to north when the coil is 10 cm from the center of the compass. Adjust the current with the potentiometer. Once you have recorded the measurement open the switch to stop the current.

5. Put the steel pin in the coil so its head is against the coil and 10 cm from the center of the compass.

6. Adjust the distance of the permanent magnet so the compass needle is deflected 20 degrees from north. *There should be no magnets nearby, and no current in the coil for this step.*

7. Close the switch to measure and record the current it takes to return the needle to north with the steel pin in the coil.

Table 1: Electromagnet current with and without the steel pin

Current with bare coil	Current with steel pin	Difference in current	Percent difference

7 Thinking about what you observed

a. How did the steel pin affect the magnetic force created by the coil? Was the magnetic force reduced, increased, or did it stay about the same? Use your observations to support your answer.

b. *Class discussion question*
The force produced by an electromagnet *could* be a different kind of force than that produced by a permanent magnet. For example wind and springs make forces that are different than magnetism. How does this experiment *support* the conclusion that the force from the electromagnet and permanent magnet are actually the same kind force?

Electromagnetic Forces

Question for this Investigation:

How does an electric motor work?

Electric motors are used in many devices you use every day. In this Investigation you will build a simple electric motor and learn how it works. The concepts you learn with the simple motor also apply to other electric motors.

Materials

- Permanent magnet
- D battery
- Rubber bands
- Metric ruler
- Modeling clay
- Sand paper
- Varnished magnet wire
- Paper clips
- Timer and photogate

1 ▸ Making the base

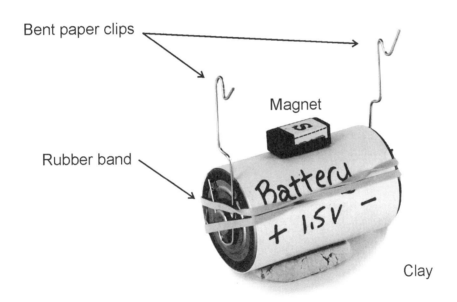

Bent paper clips

Magnet

Rubber band

Battery
+ 1.5V −

Clay

1. Bend the two paper clips so they look like the drawing.
2. Fasten them with rubber bands so they contact the positive and negative terminals of the battery.
3. Set the battery on a lump of clay so it stands up.
4. Stick a magnet to the top of the battery with another lump of clay.
5. Your motor base is complete!

2 ▲ Making the coil

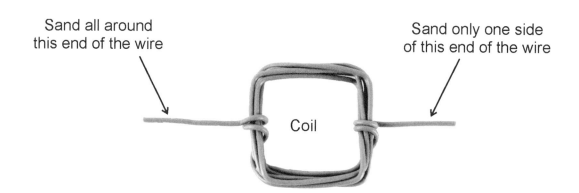

Sand all around this end of the wire

Sand only one side of this end of the wire

Coil

1. Cut 1 meter of magnet wire. This wire has a painted insulation on it so the surface looks like copper metal but is really covered in a thin layer of insulator.
2. Wrap the wire around the square form of the modeling clay with one end sticking out 4 cm or so.
3. Keep wrapping until you have only 4-5 cm left.
4. Remove your coil from the form and wrap the ends of the wire a few turns around the sides of the coil to keep things together. There should be about 3 cm of wire on each side of the coil.
5. Take some sand paper and sand off all the varnish on one wire.
6. Sand of the varnish on ONE SIDE ONLY of the other end of the wire.
7. Adjust the wires until the coil balances as well as you can get it.
8. Your coil is done!

3 ▲ Making the motor work

1. Set the coil into the paper clips so it is free to spin.
2. Adjust the height of the paper clips until the coil rotates just above the magnet.
3. The motor should spin! Adjust the balance by bending the wires or paper clips.

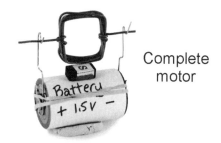

Complete motor

4 ▲ Thinking about what you observed

a. Explain the force acting on the coil when there is current flowing. What creates the force?

b. Why was it important to sand only one side of the wire on one end of the coil.

c. See if you can hold a photogate so the spinning coil breaks the light beam. Perform an experiment to measure the speed of your motor.

d. Try adding a second magnet. Does this make the motor go faster, slower, or about the same? What observations did you make that support your answer?

Electromagnetic Induction

Question for this Investigation:

How does an electric generator work?

Changing electric currents can cause magnets to move, as in the electric motor. The reverse is also true. Changing magnetism can cause electric currents to flow. This is the principle on which the electric generator works. In this investigation you will build a simple electric generator and test how it works.

Materials

- Magnets
- Electromagnet coil
- Ripcord Generator kit
- Digital meter and leads
- Electric circuits kit
- Timer
- Safety goggles

 Making a generator

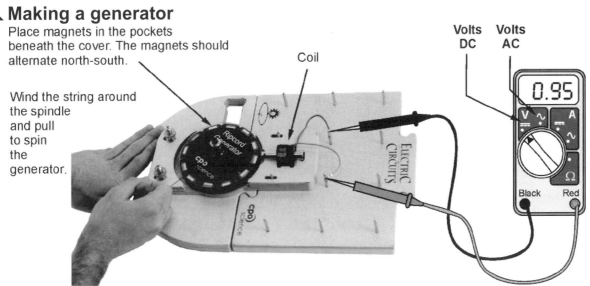

Safety Tip: (1) Wear safety glasses, (2) Pull the ripcord with a straight motion, pulling directly away from the spindle, (3) Firmly hold the base of the generator assembly and circuit board.

1. Attach the Ripcord Generator assembly to the circuit board.
2. Connect the meter and coil as shown in the diagram.
3. Put four magnets in the rotor, evenly spaced and alternating north/south.
4. Wrap a string around the spindle and pull it to set the rotor turning.
5. Observe the voltage with the meter set to first "Volts DC" and then "Volts AC"

 Thinking about what you observed

a. Explain the difference between AC and DC electricity.

b. Is electricity produced by the magnets at rest or only by motion of the magnets?

c. Does the generator make AC or DC electricity? Support your answer with your observations.

Voltage and speed

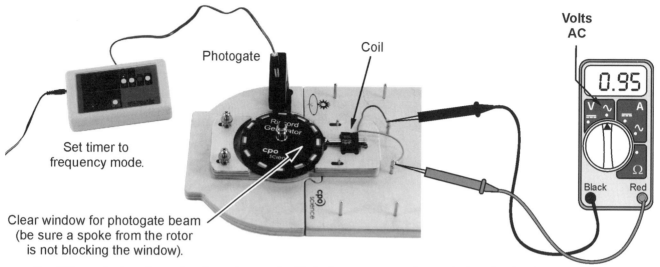

Photogate

Coil

Volts AC

0.95

Set timer to frequency mode.

Black   Red

Clear window for photogate beam
(be sure a spoke from the rotor
is not blocking the window).

1. Slip a photogate under the rotor so the light beam passes through the slot in the cover of the rotor. Set the Timer to measure frequency. This tells you how many times per second the light beam is broken. The beam is broken once per turn.

2. Start the rotor spinning. As it slows down record the AC voltage produced by the generator at different speeds. This will take several people cooperating to do. You will need to develop and practice a technique for recording numbers that are changing rapidly.

Table 1: Voltage versus speed data

Frequency from Timer (Hz)	Rotational speed (rev. per sec.)	Voltage produced (V AC)

 Thinking about what you observed

a. Does the voltage produced depend on the speed? Support your answer with your observations.

b. Make a graph of voltage versus speed. Is the graph a straight line or a curve?

 Changing the design

1. Try different numbers of magnets.
2. Try moving the steel pin to make different sized gaps between the pin and the rotor.

 Thinking about what you observed

a. Which changes you made in part 5 have the largest effect on the voltage produced?

b. Explain why changing one thing made a large difference while changing the other did not. The answer is not obvious so this should be a class discussion question.

7 ▲ Building different generators

In the next part you are going to test different configurations of magnets at different speeds.

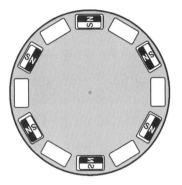

6 magnets - alternating

12 magnets - alternating

12 magnets - same side out

1. Try different combinations of magnets in the rotor.
2. Try facing all the magnets the same way.
3. Measure the voltage at a constant speed for each different magnet configuration.

Table 2: Voltage for different magnet configurations

Magnet configuration (describe)	Rotational frequency (Hz)	Voltage produced (V AC)

8 ▲ Thinking about what you observed

a. If the number of magnets is increased from 6 to 12, what change do you expect in the voltage? Assume the magnets alternate north-south.

b. Suppose you have 6 magnets (alternate north-south) and double the speed. What change do you expect in the voltage?

c. Suppose you change from 6 to 12 magnets and also double the speed. What change do you expect in the voltage?

d. Propose a relationship that accounts for the voltage produced at different speeds and magnet configurations. This should be a class discussion question.

e. What change in voltage do you expect when changing from 12 magnets with alternating north-south to 12 magnets all facing the same way? Why?

The Magnetic Field

18A

Question for this Investigation:

Does magnetic force spread out in the area around a permanent magnet?

How does one magnet "know" another magnet is there? The answer took a long time to discover and has shaped much of our understanding of physics. This Investigation will explore the concept of a field with the magnetic field as an example. Almost all of what you learn applies to other fields we know to exist, such as gravitational fields and electric fields.

Materials

- Magnets
- Tape
- Compass
- Cardboard 50 cm x 70 cm or larger

1 ▲ Making a map of a magnetic field

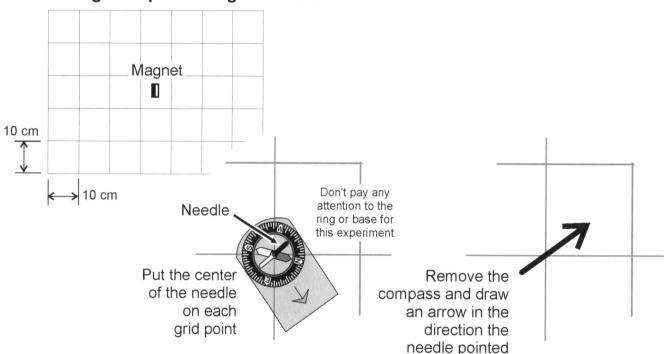

1. Draw and label *x* and *y*-axes on two perpendicular edges of the cardboard. Draw a grid of 10 cm boxes.
2. Tape the board to a table so it cannot move.
3. Tape a magnet to the center of the cardboard with the north-south axis parallel to the long side of the cardboard.
4. Put the compass on a grid point so the center of the needle is over the grid point.
5. Observe the angle of the needle then remove the compass and draw an arrow in the direction the north (colored) end of the needle was facing.
6. Map out the whole board one grid point at a time.

Thinking about what you observed

a. The arrow of the compass shows you the direction of the force felt
by the _____ pole of another magnet. (Fill in the blank with the word "north" or "south")

b. The lines of magnetic field point away from _____ and toward _____ magnetic poles.
(Fill in the blanks with the word "north" or "south")

c. Why do all the arrows far from the magnet point in the same direction?

d. Research and give a one sentence definition of a "field" as the term is used in physics. This may be a
class discussion question.

e. Describe two basic kinds of fields and give the difference between them. The magnetic force around a
magnet is an example of one and the temperature around a candle flame is an example of the other.

3 **The electric field**

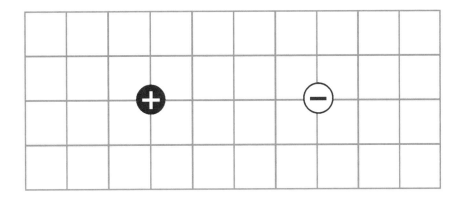

a. Draw arrows on each of the grid points in the diagram above to show the force felt by a positive electric
charge. This is a diagram of the electric field.

 The gravitational field

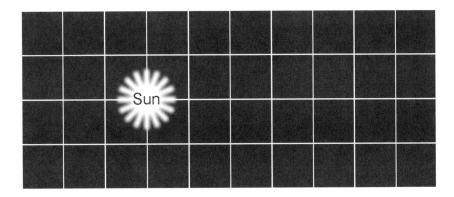

a. Draw arrows on each of the grid points in the diagram above to show the force felt by an asteroid
moving near the sun. This is a diagram of the gravitational field.

Using Fields

18B

Question for this Investigation:

What does a field tell you about what created it?

There is a very important law in physics that says if you can measure every detail of a field then you can deduce everything about the object that created it (the source). In many cases the field is what we "see" and we want to know about the object that created the field. This Investigation you will use magnetic fields to solve a puzzle, demonstrating how fields are related to the objects that create them.

Materials

- Magnets
- Tape
- Compass
- Meter stick
- Cardboard 60 cm x 90 cm

 Making the puzzle

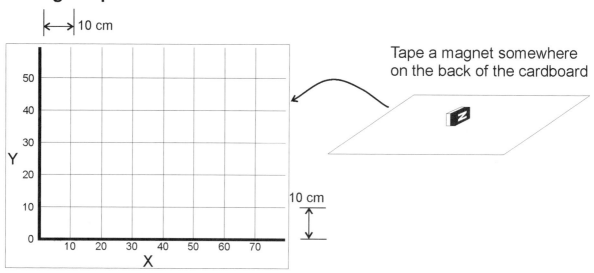

1. Draw and label *x* and *y*-axes on two perpendicular edges of the cardboard. Draw and label grid with 10 cm boxes.

2. Tape a magnet to the opposite side of the cardboard with its north-south axes parallel to the surface. Do not show any other groups where you have placed your magnet.

3. The magnet may be anywhere on the cardboard, but stay 10 centimeters from the edge.

4. Measure and write down the (x, y) coordinates of your magnet, and draw a diagram showing the exact angle of the north-south axis.

 Thinking about what you are going to do

a. Exchange your puzzle with another group

b. Locate the magnet on the cardboard grid you receive and deduce its north- south angle using only a compass to detect the field created by the magnet.

Solving the puzzle

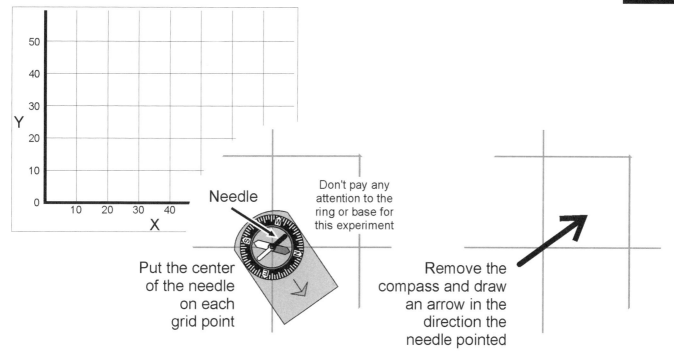

Needle

Put the center of the needle on each grid point

Don't pay any attention to the ring or base for this experiment

Remove the compass and draw an arrow in the direction the needle pointed

1. Put the compass on each of the grid points so the center of the needle is over the grid point.
2. Observe the angle of the needle then removes the compass and draw an arrow in the direction the north end of the needle was facing.
3. Map out the whole board.

 Thinking about what you observed

a. How can you use the map you made to determine the location and orientation of the hidden magnet? The diagrams below may assist you to interpret the field patterns you drew.

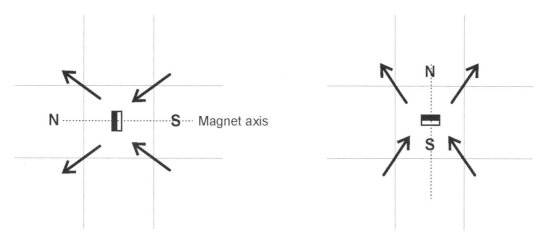

N ⋯⋯ S⋯ Magnet axis

N

S

b. Sketch the magnetic axis of the magnet on your map

c. Flip the cardboard grid over and check your results. Did you get the location and orientation correct?.

Harmonic Motion

Question for this Investigation

How does physics describe the repeating motion of a pendulum or swing?

Harmonic motion is motion that repeats in cycles. Many important systems in nature and many useful inventions rely on harmonic motion. For example, the phases of the moon and the seasons are caused by Earth's harmonic motion. This Investigation will explore harmonic motion using a pendulum. The concepts you learn with the pendulum will also apply to other examples of harmonic motion.

Materials

- Physics stand
- Graph paper
- Timer and 1 photogate
- Pendulum apparatus

Make a pendulum

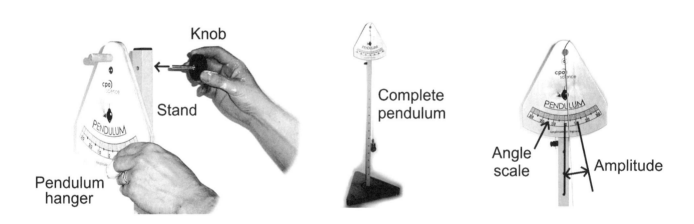

Start the pendulum swinging and watch it for a minute. Think about how to describe the motion.

a. Write one sentence about the motion using the word "cycle."

b. The *amplitude* is the maximum amount the pendulum swings away from its resting position. The resting position is straight down. One way to measure amplitude is the angle the pendulum moves away from center. Write one sentence describing the motion of your pendulum using the word "amplitude."

c. Draw a sequence of sketches that describe one complete cycle using arrows to indicate the direction the pendulum is going at that point in the cycle.

2 ▲ Oscillators and period

a. Use the stopwatch to measure the period of your pendulum. Time ten cycles Do three trials and use Table 1 to record your data.

b. Divide the average time for ten cycles by 10 to get the period.

c. Write a one sentence description of how you measured the period.

Count 10 cycles

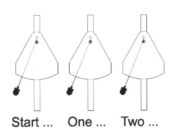

Start ... One ... Two ...

Divide time by 10

example
period = 15.20 sec ÷ 10
= 1.52 seconds

Timer in stopwatch mode

Table 1: Pendulum period data: Time for 10 cycles (sec)

Trial 1	Trial 2	Trial 3	Average
Period of pendulum (average divided by10)			

3 ▲ Measuring period with a photogate

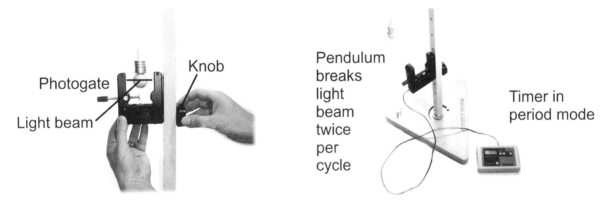

Photogate

Knob

Light beam

Pendulum breaks light beam twice per cycle

Timer in period mode

1. Attach the photogate as shown in the diagram. The pendulum breaks the light beam when it swings through the photogate. Try to keep the string length close to the length you used in part 2.

2. Put the Timer in period mode and let the pendulum swing through the light beam.

3. The reset (O) button does two things. If you press reset once the display freezes allowing you to write down a number before it changes. Pressing reset a second time starts another measurement.

4 ▲ Thinking about what you observed

a. Write down the time measurement you get from the Timer.

b. Is the time you get from the Timer the period of the pendulum? Explain why the time is or is not the period of the pendulum (hint: compare to your results from part 2).

c. Explain how the time measured by the Timer is related to the period of the pendulum.

93

5 **What variables affect the period of a pendulum?**

You can change several things about the pendulum.

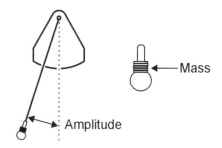

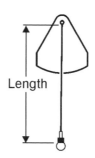

- The amplitude (angle)
- The mass (add or subtract washers)
- The length of the string (measure as shown)

a. Think of three experiments you can do to see what variables affect the period of the pendulum. Write down one sentence describing each experiment.

b. Do the three experiments and record the measurements you make to assess the effect of changing each variable.

c. Write a sentence about the effect of each variable. Write a second sentence explaining how the data you took support the statement you made about each variable. For example,

"We found that changing _____ had almost no effect on the period. We know because when we changed _____ from _____ to _____ the period only changed from _____ to _____, which is a very small difference.

6 **Sketch a graph of the motion using amplitude and period**

The most common type of graph puts amplitude on the vertical (*y*) axis and time on the horizontal (*x*) axis. Follow the steps in the diagram below to sketch a graph showing the motion of the pendulum.

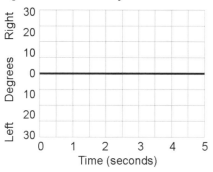

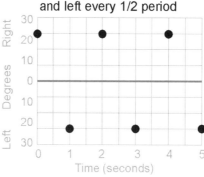

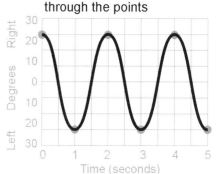

a. How many complete cycles does your graph show?

b. Describe how to determine the amplitude of motion from a harmonic motion graph.

c. Describe how to determine the period from a harmonic motion graph.

d. What is the amplitude and period of the motion shown on the graph in the diagram above?

Natural Frequency

Question for this Investigation:

How do force and mass affect harmonic motion?

Newton's second law gives the relationship between motion, force, and mass. While the second law still applies, there are new effects that result when the second law is applied to systems in harmonic motion. This Investigation will explore the idea of natural frequency, and how the natural frequency of a system is related to Newton's laws.

Materials

- Physics stand
- Two 1/4" × 6" steel rods

- Timer and 1 photogate
- 4 rubber bands (#33, 1/8 × 3 1/2")

- Two steel washers. Washers for 1/2" bolts are about the right size and mass.

 Make an oscillator

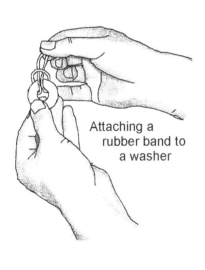

Attaching a rubber band to a washer

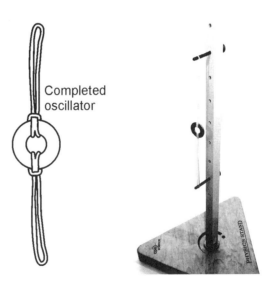

Completed oscillator

Attach your oscillator to the Stand with 2 metal rods set 6 holes (30 cm) apart

1. Fix two rubber bands onto opposite sides of a washer as shown in the diagram.
2. Stretch the rubber bands a few times to "break them in."
3. Set the two steel rods into the stand so they are 6 holes apart. The washer is suspended by the stretched rubber bands.
4. Pull the washer about 1 centimeter to one side. Release the washer and observe its motion.

2 ▲ Measure the natural frequency

You can use a photogate to measure the natural frequency by measuring the period of your oscillator. Remember, period and frequency are related (*frequency* = 1 ÷ *period*).

The measurement is tricky to do. You have to hold the photogate so the washer breaks the light beam just once per cycle.

1. Nudge the rubber bands around until the washer oscillates back and forth without twisting much. Practice your technique until you can get the washer to oscillate back and forth with an amplitude of about 1 centimeter

2. Hold a photogate near the edge of the oscillating washer so the washer breaks the light beam once per cycle. You should see the light on the photogate flash red and green as the washer breaks the beam.

3. Set the Timer to measure the period of the oscillation. Record three measurements and take the average.

4. Convert period to frequency.

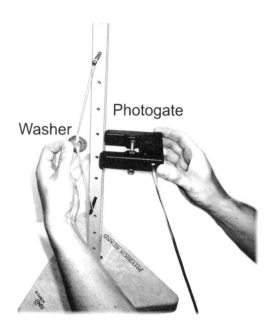

Table 1: Natural frequency data (Hz) for 1 washer with 2 rubber bands

Trial 1 Period (sec)	Trial 2 Period (sec)	Trial 3 Period (sec)	Average Period (sec)
		Natural Frequency (Hz)	

3 ▲ Thinking about what you observed

a. Does the washer-and-rubber-band oscillator have a natural frequency? How do you know?

b. Explain in one or two sentences how you measured the natural frequency. (Hint: describe the washer's motion relative to the photogate.)

c. What would happen to the natural frequency if you made the rubber bands stronger? Would the natural frequency get higher, lower, or stay about the same? Explain your reasoning in a few sentences.

d. What would happen to the natural frequency if you made the washer heavier by adding more mass? Would the natural frequency get higher, lower, or stay about the same? Explain your reasoning in a few sentences.

4 ▲ Changing the force in your oscillator

Completed 4-band oscillator

Rubber bands

Washer

Rubber bands should be snug on washer and in opposite pairs. Pre-stretch the rubber bands before making any measurements.

1. Tie a second set of rubber bands around the washer as shown.
2. Measure the natural frequency with the rubber bands stretched the same distance as part 2.

5 ▲ How the natural frequency depends on mass and force

1. Use the techniques of part 2 to measure the natural period of your oscillator for the four combinations shown in Table 2.
2. To be consistent, the rubber bands should be stretched the same distance for all trials.

1 Washer
2 Rubber bands

2 Washers
2 Rubber bands

1 Washer
4 Rubber bands

2 Washers
4 Rubber bands

Table 2: Natural Period and Frequency Data (sec)

	2 Rubber bands 1 Washer	4 Rubber bands 1 Washer	2 Rubber bands 2 Washers	4 Rubber bands 2 Washers
Trial 1				
Trial 2				
Trial 3				
Average period				
Natural frequency (Hz)				

6 ▲ Thinking about what you observed

a. Did the results agree with your answers to questions 3d and 3e? If not, give new answers based on your observations.

b. The natural frequency depends on the ratio of two variables. One from the rubber bands and one mostly from the steel washer(s). What are the two variables and how should they be arranged as a ratio?

Waves

20A

Question for this Investigation:

What are the properties of waves?

Waves are oscillations that move from one place to another. Like oscillations, waves also have the properties of frequency and amplitude. In this Investigation, you will explore waves on strings and in water. What you learn applies to all other types of waves as well.

Materials

- Timer
- Metal Slinky® toy spring
- Piece of elastic 1.5 to 2 mm in dia. and 3 m long
- 0-5 N spring scale
- 20 steel washers (1/2" size)
- 19 #16 rubber bands (1/8 × 3 1/2" size)
- A length of 1" plastic pipe cut to fit your ripple tray
- Some food coloring, a jug for mixing, and water
- A shallow tray at least 50 cm × 50 cm in size (20"). Larger is better.
- Enough blocks to cross the tray

1 Making a wave pulse

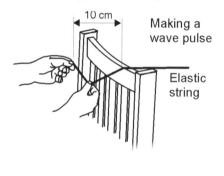

10 cm

Making a wave pulse

Elastic string

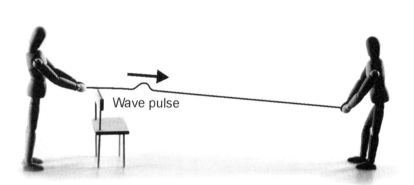

Wave pulse

1. Take one end of the elastic string and make a knot for attaching a spring scale that can measure 5 newtons of force. The string should be stretched so that the scale reads 1 newton.

2. Your partner should rest the other end of the string against the top of a chair. Pull the string down about 10 centimeters and release it.

3. A wave pulse should move down the string toward the spring scale.

2 Thinking about what you observed

a. How is the motion of a wave pulse different from the motion of a moving object such as a car. (HINT: What is it that moves in the case of a wave?)

b. What happens to the wave pulse when it hits the far end of the string? Watch carefully. Does the pulse stay on the same side of the string or flip to the other side? Use the word "reflect" in your answer.

3 ▸ Transverse waves

A _transverse wave_ has its oscillations perpendicular to the direction the wave moves.

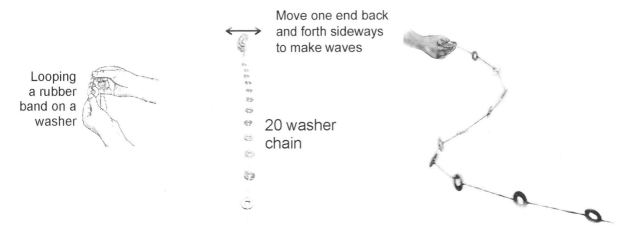

Looping a rubber band on a washer

Move one end back and forth sideways to make waves

20 washer chain

1. Take 20 steel washers and rubber bands and chain them together so each washer is connected to the next one by a rubber band.

2. Stretch the chain between two people until it is about 1 1/2 times its unstretched length.

3. One person should shake their end of the chain sideways with an amplitude of about 5 cm (2"). The other person holding the chain should keep their end fixed.

4. Change the frequency at which the chain is shaken. You should see wave patterns appear on the chain at certain oscillation frequencies.

5. See if you can get wave patterns with one, two, and three bumps in the middle.

6. Use the stopwatch (Timer) to measure the frequency of each wave. Time ten cycles and divide by ten to get the period. Frequency = 1 ÷ period. This works best if the person who is shaking counts cycles out loud. For example, "ready, set, go, one, two, three,..."

Table 1: Wave Frequency and Period Data

Wave Pattern	Trial 1 Time for 10 cycles (sec)	Trial 2 Time for 10 cycles (sec)	Trial 3 Time for 10 cycles (sec)	Average Time for 10 cycles (sec)	Period (sec)	Frequency (Hz)

4 ▸ Thinking about what you observed

a. Imagine you removed one rubber band in the middle, making two unconnected chains. Do you think the wave could cross the break. Discuss the reasoning behind your answer in a few sentences.

b. Why does the wave move along the chain from one washer to the next?

c. Use the data you collected to complete Table 1 and calculate the natural frequency and period of the different wave patterns you observed.

d. Did you find a relationship between the frequencies at which you had to shake the chain to get the three different wave patterns? What relationship did you find?

5 ⮞ Waves in water

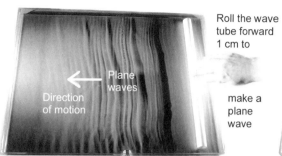

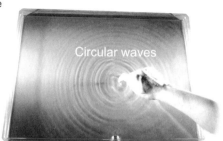

Wood blocks

1. Fill a flat tray with about one-half centimeter of colored water. The color helps you see the waves.

2. Roll the wave tube forward about 1 cm in a smooth motion. This launches a nearly straight wave called a *plane wave* across the tray.

3. Next, poke the surface of the water with your fingertip. Disturbing a single point on the surface of the water makes a *circular wave* that moves outward from where you touched the water.

4. Arrange two wood blocks so they cross the tray leaving a 1 cm opening between them.

5. Make a plane wave that moves toward the blocks. Observe what happens to the wave that goes through the opening.

6 ⮞ Thinking about what you observed

a. The wave front of a water wave is an imaginary line drawn to show the shape of the crest of one wave. Draw a sketch that shows the wave front of your plane wave. Also on your sketch, draw an arrow that shows the direction the wave moves.

b. Is the wave front parallel or perpendicular to the direction the wave moves?

c. Draw another sketch that shows the circular wave fronts and include at least four arrows that show the direction in which each part of the wave moves.

d. At every point along the wave, are the wave fronts more parallel or perpendicular to the direction in which the circular wave moves?

e. Sketch the shape of the wave fronts before and after wave passes through the 1 cm opening.

f. Does the wave change shape when it passes through the opening? If you see any change, your answer should say what kind of shape the wave changes into.

Resonance and Standing Waves

Question for this Investigation

How do we make and control waves?

Waves can be _reflected_ from boundaries, such as the clamped end of a string. If the conditions are just right, a _standing wave_ forms. A standing wave is an extended oscillation where a whole system can move with a single wave pattern. In this Investigation, you will use a standing wave to explore the connection between the frequency of a wave and its wavelength. You will use a vibrating string because the standing waves are large enough to see easily. However, what you learn applies to all other types of waves as well.

Materials

- Physics stand
- Sound and waves kit
- Timer with AC adapter
- Photogate wire
- 0 - 5N spring scale

1 ▶ Setting up a standing wave experiment

Connect the Timer to the sound and waves generator as shown in the diagram. The telephone cord connects the Timer and wave generator. The black wire goes between the wave generator and the wiggler.

1. Attach the fiddle head to the top of the stand as high as it will go.
2. Attach the wiggler to the bottom of the stand as low as it will go.
3. Stretch the elastic string a little (5 to 10 centimeters) and attach the free end to the fiddle head. Loosen the knob until you can slide the string between any two of the washers. GENTLY tighten the knob just enough to hold the string.
4. Turn on the Timer using the AC adapter.
5. Use the button on the lower left of the front panel to set the wave generator to _waves_. The wiggler should start to wiggle back and forth, shaking the string.
6. Set the Timer to measure frequency. You should get a reading of about 10 Hz, meaning the wiggler is oscillating 10 times per second.
7. Try adjusting the frequency of the wiggler with the frequency control on the wave generator. If you watch the string, you will find that interesting patterns form at certain frequencies.

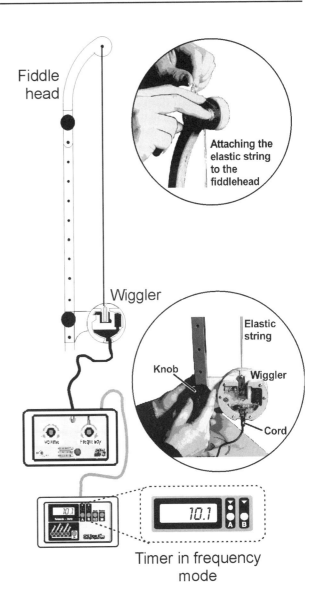

Fiddle head

Attaching the elastic string to the fiddlehead

Wiggler

Elastic string

Knob

Wiggler

Cord

Timer in frequency mode

2. Thinking about what you observed

At certain frequencies, the vibrating string forms standing wave patterns called *harmonics*. The first harmonic has one bump, the second harmonic has two bumps, and so on.

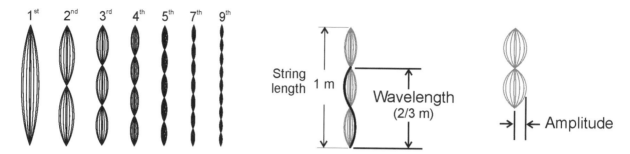

a. The string is 1 meter long. The *wavelength*, λ, is the length of one complete wave. Without using a meter stick, how can you determine the wavelength of each standing wave?

3. Finding the standing waves

You noticed that the standing waves only occur at certain special frequencies. The wiggler applies a periodic force to the string. When the periodic force matches the natural frequency of the string, a large response develops (resonance).

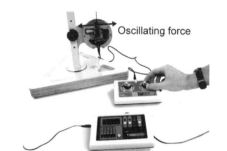

1. Use the frequency control to find the first through the eighth harmonics of the string (at least).

2. Record the frequency and wavelength for each harmonic in Table 1. You should fine-tune the frequency to get the largest amplitude wave before recording the data. Look for harmonics 2 to 6 before looking for the first one. The first harmonic, also called the *fundamental*, is hard to find with exactness. Once you have the frequencies for the others, they provide a clue for finding the frequency of the first harmonic.

Table 1: Frequency, harmonic, and wavelength data

Harmonic #	Frequency (Hz)	Wavelength (m)	Frequency times wavelength
1			
2			
3			

4. Thinking about what you observed

a. In one or two sentences, describe how the frequencies of the different harmonic patterns are related.

b. Why is the word *fundamental* chosen as another name for the first harmonic?

c. Give an equation relating frequency (*f*) and wavelength (λ) that best describes your observations.

d. If the frequency increases by a factor of two, what happens to the wavelength?

e. Propose a meaning for the number you get by multiplying frequency and wavelength.

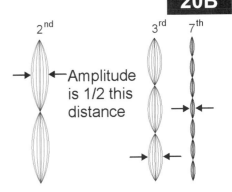

5 Frequency and energy

Waves are useful because they carry energy from one place to another. The energy of a wave can also carry information such as a voice signal from a cell phone or a TV picture.

1. Set up several wave patterns and measure the amplitude for each harmonic.

2. Measure at least 5 different harmonics, including the 6th or higher.

Table 2: Frequency vs. amplitude data

Harmonic #	Frequency (Hz)	Amplitude (cm)

6 Thinking about what you observed

a. What happens to the amplitude of the waves as their frequency increases?

b. How does the energy of a wave depend on its frequency if the amplitude stays constant? How is your answer supported by your observations of the vibrating string?

7 Resonance

The diagram shows a useful way to think about pushing a swing. The person pushing applies a periodic force to the swing, just like the wiggler does to the vibrating string. Like the string, a swing is a system in harmonic motion. If the push is applied at the swing's natural frequency, the amplitude grows large, like the standing wave on the string. The response of a swing to a periodic push is an example of *resonance*. The harmonics on the vibrating string are another example of resonance. Resonance happens when the force applied to a system matches its natural frequency. We use resonance to create waves with specific frequencies, such as in a musical instrument, cell phone, or microwave oven.

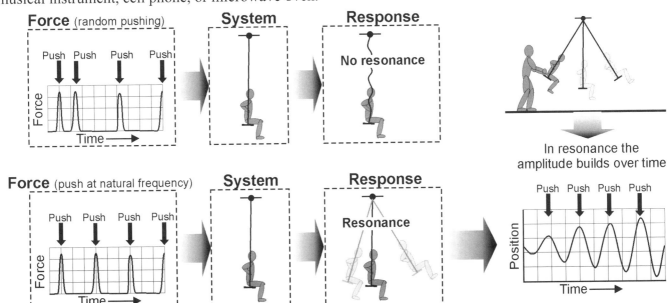

The Properties of Sound

Question for this Investigation

How do we know sound is a wave?

The human ear is a sensitive detector of sound. Like other waves, sound has properties of frequency, amplitude, wavelength, and speed. This Investigation will explore some of the many properties of sound.

Materials

- Sound and waves kit
- Timer with AC adapter
- Graph paper

 What do different frequencies sound like?

1. Connect your sound generator to a Timer set to measure frequency. Connect a speaker to the sound generator.

2. When you turn the Timer on, you should hear a sound and the Timer should read a frequency near 440 Hz.

3. Try adjusting the frequency and volume controls. Listen to the sounds as you watch the frequency measurements on the Timer.

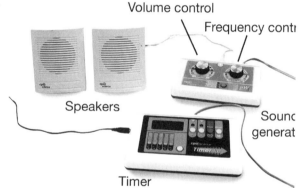

4. Listen to many frequencies and decide on three that represent sounds that you hear as low, medium, and high pitch. Don't try to be too exact because the words "low," "medium," and "high" are not well defined. It is difficult to agree exactly on anything that is based completely on individual human perception.

Table 1: How we hear frequencies of sound

Description	Frequency (Hz)
Low	
Medium	
High	
Very high	

2 ▶ How high can you hear?

Your teacher has a sound generator that can make frequencies up to 20,000 Hz.

1. When the teacher asks, raise your hand if you can hear the sound. Do not raise your hand if you cannot hear it.

2. Someone will be appointed to count hands and survey the class to see what fraction of students can hear each frequency of sound.

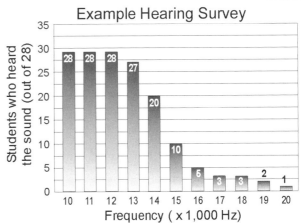

Example Hearing Survey

3 ▶ Thinking about what you observed

a. Make a histogram showing your class response to frequencies between 10,000 and 20,000 Hz. You should have 5 bars, one per 2,000 Hz.

b. Do you think the method of counting raised hands is likely to give an accurate result? Give at least one reason you believe the method is either good or bad.

4 ▶ The interference of two sound waves

How do we know sound is a wave? What experimental evidence proves sound is a wave? Suppose two sounds reach your ear at the same time. Interference occurs when more than one wave is present at the same time, in the same place.

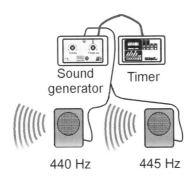

Sound generator   Timer

440 Hz   445 Hz

1. The teacher will set up two sound waves generated by one machine set to operate in "beat" mode. One sound wave will be at 440 Hz and the other will be at 445 Hz.

2. Listen to the 440 Hz sound by itself.

3. Listen to the 445 Hz sound by itself.

4. Listen to the combination of 440 Hz and 445 Hz together.

5. The teacher will keep one sound at 445 Hz and adjust the frequency of the other one between 430 and 450 Hz. Listen to the combination.

5. Thinking about what you observed

The oscillations of loud and soft you hear from the two sound waves are called _beats_.
Beats are caused by small differences in frequency between multiple sounds heard at the same time.

Why we hear beats

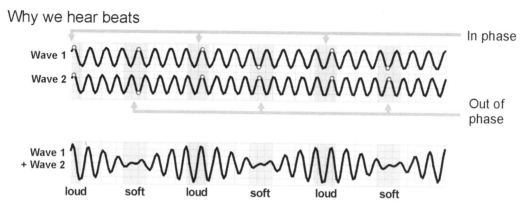

a. Read about beats. Using the diagram above, write a few sentences explaining why beats occur and how they are created by the wave properties of sound.

b. If the two frequencies are exactly the same do you hear beats?

c. Would you expect to hear beats from an 800 Hz and a 805 Hz sound played together? Would you expect to hear beats from an 800 Hz and a 845 Hz sound played together? Explain why or why not.

d. What determines the frequency of the beats?

6. Finding a mystery frequency

When two waves are close, but not exactly matched in frequency, you hear beats. Musicians use beats to tune their instruments. When two sounds have the same frequency there are no beats!

Mystery frequency

1. The instructor will set a sound generator to play a mystery frequency.

2. Use your sound generator to figure out the mystery frequency by listening for beats.

3. The closer you get to the mystery frequency, the slower the beats will become. When you are exactly matched with the mystery frequency the beats will be so slow you can no longer hear them.

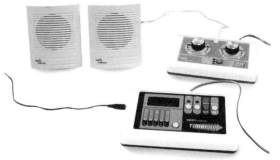

Search frequency (you control)

HINT: The frequency knob on the wave generator moves in 1 Hz increments IF you turn it very slowly, one click at a time.

Wave Properties of Sound

Questions for this Investigation:

How are the properties of waves used in the design of musical instruments?

There are many situations when we want to make sound of a certain frequency, such as with a musical instrument. This Investigation will explore how sounds can be controlled by the shape of objects.

Materials

- Sound and waves kit
- 10-20 #16 rubber bands
- Timer with AC adapter
- 1/2" copper pipe, at least 4' for a 3-bar chime
- Pipe cutter
- 4 Plastic straws
- Scissors

1 Controlling frequency and wavelength

Make the end of the straw into a point

cut off these two triangles

Pinch the edges to flatten the straw so the points of the triangle are nearly flat against each other.

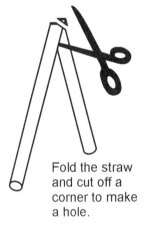
Fold the straw and cut off a corner to make a hole.

1. Make a straw kazoo and make some sound with it (diagram above).

2. Now take a pair of scissors and cut a few centimeters off the open end of the kazoo. What happens to the frequency of the sound it makes?

3. Make another straw kazoo. Take the scissors and cut a small hole exactly in the middle of your kazoo. Cover the hole with your finger. Blow through the kazoo. Cover and uncover the hole. What happens to the sound? (Hint: What is vibrating in the straw is a length of air.)

2 Thinking about what you observed

a. How is sound created by the kazoo?

b. Why does the frequency change with the length of the straw? Think back to your experiments with the vibrating string.

c. Identify at least three musical instruments that use vibrating air columns or objects of different lengths to make sounds of different frequencies.

107

3 Complex sounds

We rarely hear only one sound wave at a time. Our brains and ears are constantly processing sound from many sources, at many frequencies and intensity levels.

1. Turn down the volume on the sound generator so that you cannot hear the sound but you can still read the frequency on the Timer.

2. Each group in the class will be given a different frequency to tune to. Tune your frequency using the timer until you are within +/- 1 Hz.

3. Your instructor will tell each group to their volume turn up or down. Don't change your frequency.

4 Thinking about what you heard

a. Describe the sound of the four frequencies 264 Hz, 330 Hz, 396 Hz, and 528 Hz when you hear them together.

b. Describe the sound of the four frequencies 264 Hz, 317 Hz, 396 Hz, and 528 Hz when you hear them together.

c. Contrast the two sounds. Does one sound more happy or sad compared with the other? Does one sound spookier than the other? Which combination reminds you more of spring, which of fall?

5 Musical scales

The notes of a musical scale are a special set of frequencies that are related to each other by ratios. Musicians in a band can play together because all their instruments are tuned to the same musical scale. These scales are in the *key* of C which means the first note of each scale is the note C.

C major scale	C	D	E	F	G	A	B	C
Frequency (Hz)	264	297	330	352	396	440	495	528
Ratio to C-264	$1/1$	$9/8$	$5/4$	$4/3$	$3/2$	$5/3$	$15/8$	$2/1$

C minor scale	C	D	E♭	F	G	A♭	B♭	C
Frequency (Hz)	264	297	317	352	396	422	475	528
Ratio to C-264	$1/1$	$9/8$	$6/5$	$4/3$	$3/2$	$8/5$	$9/5$	$2/1$

6 Thinking about what you heard

a. What notes have frequencies of 264, 330, and 396 Hz? What is this combination of 3 notes called?

b. What notes have frequencies of 264, 317, and 396 Hz? What is this combination of 3 notes called?

c. What is the relationship between the frequencies of notes with the same name?

Making an instrument

For the last part of the Investigation you will make a musical instrument that plays the scale.

Table 1: Musical chimes

Column 1 Note number	Column 2 Frequency ratio	Column 3 Length of first chime	Column 4 Length ratio	Length of chime for this note (= Col. 3 x Col. 4)
1	1		1.00	
2	9/8		0.94	
3	5/4		0.89	
4	4/3		0.87	
5	3/2		0.82	
6	5/3		0.77	
7	15/8		0.73	
8	2		0.71	

1. Decide on the length of your longest chime. Write the length in column 3 of Table 1.

2. Calculate the length of your second chime by multiplying the length in column 3 by the length ratio in column 4.

3. Repeat the calculation for the rest of the notes in your chime.

4. Follow the procedure in the diagram to cut your pipe into the right lengths.

5. Tie your chimes together with loops of rubber bands that are about 1/5 of the way in from each end.

6. Make a hammer to play your chime from a small wooden ball and a stick.

Congratulations! You have made a musical instrument.

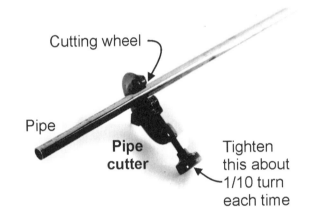

Cutting wheel

Pipe

Pipe cutter

Tighten this about 1/10 turn each time

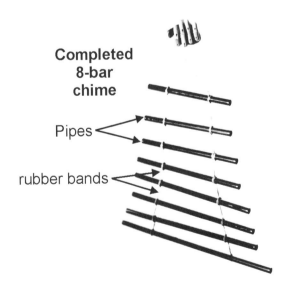

Completed 8-bar chime

Pipes

rubber bands

 Thinking about what you made

a. How were the properties of waves used to design your musical instrument?

b. Do some research and find out how the length ratio is related to the frequency ratio for panpipes.

109

Light and Color

Question for this Investigation:

How is color created by light

Light is so useful and so common that we often don't think about what light is. Light has many properties, such as its ability to carry images, colors, and heat. This Investigation will examine some of the properties of light related to its color.

Materials

- Light and optics kit
- Room that may be darkened.
- TV or computer screen
- Yellow, Magenta (pink), Cyan (blue-green) clay or Play-doh™

1. Sources of light

a. Compare the light from a light bulb with the light from the same bulb when seen in a mirror. In both cases, describe the path of the light from the source to your eyes.

b. Look at your clothes. Does the light reaching your eye from your clothes originate in your clothes? Or does the light originate somewhere else?

c. Turn off all the lights, and shade the windows so it is completely dark. Can you see your clothes in the dark? What does this experiment tell you about whether your clothes give off their own light or reflect light from somewhere else?

d. Turn on a television or computer screen in a dark room. Can you see the TV or computer screen in the dark? What does this experiment tell you about whether the TV or computer screen give off their own light or reflect light from somewhere else?

How do we see colors?

Brown hair

Red ice pop

Yellow shirt (with red spots!)

Red shorts with yellow flowers

Give off light or reflect light?

Can you see a TV in a completely dark room?

INVESTIGATION

22A

2 ▶ Making colors

1. Plug the red, green, and blue LED lamps into the optics table.

2. Place the three lamps side by side on one edge of the optics table. Set one of the lenses in the middle. Set the screen (back of the mirror) at the opposite edge from the LEDs.

3. You should see three spots of color on the screen (red-green-blue). Move the lens and screen to make the three spots overlap and observe the colors on the screen.

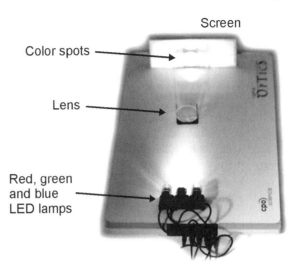

Screen

Color spots

Lens

Red, green and blue LED lamps

3 ▶ Thinking about what you observed

a. What color do you see when you mix red and green light?

b. What color do you see when you mix red and blue light?

c. What color do you see when you mix blue and green light?

d. What color is produced when all three colors of light are equally mixed?

Table 1: Mixing primary colors of light

LED color combination	Color you see
Red + Green	
Green + Blue	
Blue + Red	
Red + Green + Blue	

e. Research and explain the following terms from the diagram below: cone cells, rod cells, retina.

f. Research and explain how the eye sees white light in terms of the photoreceptors in the eye.

Photoreceptors in the eye

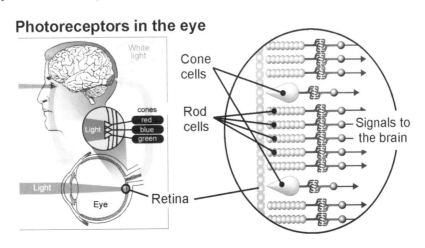

111

4 ▸ The subtractive color model (CMYK)

1. You have three colors of clay: yellow, magenta, and cyan. Take a portion the size of your fingertip of the both cyan and the magenta. Mix them together. What color do you get?

2. Mix equal amounts of cyan and yellow. What color do you get?

3. Mix equal amounts of yellow and magenta. What color do you get?

The subtractive color model (CMYK)

	Cyan	Magenta	Yellow	Black
Absorbs	Red	Green	Blue	Red, Green, Blue
Reflects	Blue, Green	Blue, Red	Red, Green	None

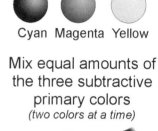

Cyan   Magenta   Yellow

Mix equal amounts of the three subtractive primary colors
(two colors at a time)

5 ▸ Thinking about what you observed

a. Explain how the mixture of magenta and cyan makes its color when seen in white light.

b. Explain how the mixture of cyan and yellow makes its color when seen in white light.

c. Explain how the mixture of yellow and magenta makes its color when seen in white light.

d. Why don't the mixed colors produce full red, green, or blue?

e. What color would appear if you looked at a mixture of magenta and cyan under a lamp that only made blue light?

f. Research how printers make colors. Do they use red, green, and blue (RGB) or cyan, magenta, yellow, and black (CMYK)? Explain why printed pictures need to use one or the other.

g. Research how computer monitors and televisions make colors. Do they use red, green, and blue (RGB) or cyan, magenta, yellow, and black (CMYK)? Explain why TV's and computer screens need to use one or the other.

Reflection and Refraction

Questions for this Investigation:

What is the difference between reflection and refraction?

Looking in a mirror we see a twin of ourselves reversed left-to-right. A fish underwater appears in a different place from where the fish really is. Both of these illusions are caused by the bending of light rays. This Investigation explores reflection and refraction, two processes that bend light rays.

Materials

- Light and optics kit
- Drop of milk
- Protractor & metric ruler
- Clear plastic cup
- Water

1 ▶ Observing the law of reflection

Setting up

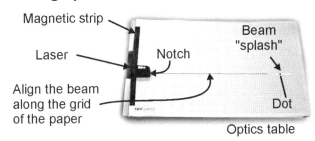

Reflecting the beam

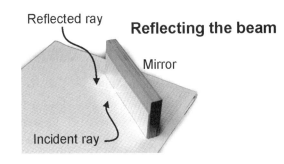

1. Set a sheet of graph paper on the optics table.
2. Connect the laser and put it on the optics table so that the base is tipped up on the magnetic strip.
3. Align the laser so the beam points down slightly and follows one horizontal line across the paper.
4. Draw a dot about 1/3 of the way along the beam "splash" on the graph paper.
5. Set the mirror on the optics table so its shiny front surface is on the dot and draw a line on the graph paper marking the front face of the mirror.
6. Use a pencil to mark the light rays going toward and away from the mirror.
7. Change the graph paper and repeat parts 1-3 with the mirror set at 3-4 different angles.

2 ▶ Thinking about what you observed

A diagram showing how light rays travel is called a *ray diagram*. Lines and arrows on a ray diagram represent rays of light.

Drawing the ray diagram

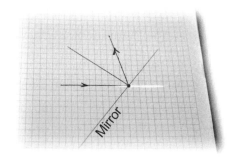

a. Draw a ray diagram showing the surface of the mirror and the light rays before and after the mirror.

b. Which is the incident ray? Label it on your ray diagram.

c. Which is the reflected ray? Label it on your ray diagram.

3 The law of reflection

a. For each ray diagram, draw a line perpendicular to the mirror surface at the point where the rays hit. This line is called the *normal line*.

b. Use a protractor to measure the angle between the normal and the incident and reflected rays.

c. Write down your own statement of the law of reflection, describing the relationship between the angles you measured.

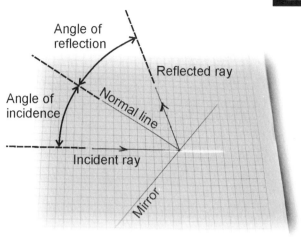

Table 1: Angles of incidence and reflection

	Diagram #1	Diagram #2	Diagram #3	Diagram #4
Angle of incidence				
Angle of reflection				

 ### 4 Light rays going through a prism

A prism is a solid piece of glass with polished surfaces. Prisms are useful for investigating how light bends when it crosses from one material to another, such as from air into glass or glass into air.

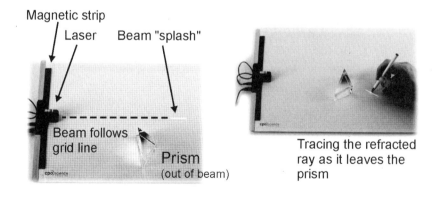

1. Set the laser put it on the optics table so that the base is tipped up on the magnetic strip. The beam should make an extended splash along the graph paper.

2. Set the prism into the laser beam so the beam comes out the opposite short side (diagram).

3. Rotate the prism in the beam and observe where the beam comes out.

5 Sketching what you observed

a. Draw at least one ray diagram showing a laser beam that is refracted passing through the prism. The _refracted ray_ is the ray that comes out of the prism.

b. Draw a ray diagram showing a laser beam that is reflected passing through the prism.

c. Draw a ray diagram showing a laser beam that is both refracted and reflected passing through the prism.

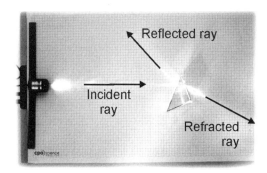

6 Seeing reflection and refraction at the same time

Both refraction and reflection often occur when light hits a boundary between materials such as the boundary between glass and air. The amount of light reflected or refracted depends on the angle at which you are looking relative to the surface.

Fold a paper card marked with A and B

The image in the prism changes as you move you head!

1. Take a piece of graph paper about the size of a business card and draw a line about 5 centimeters from one edge, dividing the rectangle in half. Draw the letter A on one side of the line and the letter B on the other side.

2. Fold the paper on the line and wrap it around one of the corners of the prism that is not a right angle.

3. Look into the prism. Move your head up and down to change the angle at which you look.

7 Thinking about what you observed

a. Draw a diagram showing the path of the light when you see the letter A.

b. Draw a diagram showing the path of the light when you see the letter B.

c. Is the image in the prism always reflected or refracted or can there be both reflection and refraction at the same time?

8 ◢ The angle of refraction

The milk makes the beam visible passing through the water.

Using an index card to locate and mark the center of the beam.

1. Fill a clear plastic cup about 1/2 with water. Add one drop (only one!) of milk to the water in the cup.

2. Set the cup on the optics table on a fresh sheet of graph paper. Use a pencil to trace around the base of the cup.

3. Shine the laser beam through the cup so it passes off-center. Use an index card to find and mark the laser beam going into and out of the cup.

4. Remove the cup and draw the ray diagram.

9 ◢ Thinking about what you observed

The change in direction of a refracted ray depends on the angle with the normal line.

a. Draw the normal line to the surface at the points where the light ray enters and leaves the cup. A round cup is convenient because the normal line points toward the center of the circle.

b. When the light is going from air into water does the ray bend toward or away from the normal?

c. When the light is going from water back into air does the ray bend toward or away from the normal?

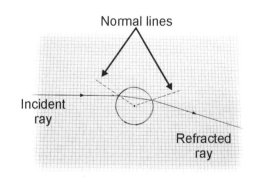

Optics

Questions for this Investigation:

How are images created by lenses and mirrors?

In optics, *objects* are real physical things that give off or reflect light rays. Images are "pictures" of objects that are formed where light rays meet. Images are created by mirrors, lenses, prisms, and other optical devices. This Investigation will look at images produced by lenses.

Materials

- Light and optics kit
- Room that may be darkened
- Metric ruler
- Lamp or sunlit window

 Making an image with a lens

A single lens makes an image of a distant light source. The image forms one focal length away from a lens.

1. Find a wall at least 5 meters away from a lamp or sunlit window. Tape a piece of white paper to the wall to create a screen for seeing the image.

2. Get one of the round convex glass lenses in the metal holders. Hold the lens at different distances from your screen. Try distances between 10 and 20 centimeters.

3. You will see a sharp image of the lamp or window on the screen when your lens is about one focal length away from the wall.

4. Use this technique to determine the focal lengths for both lenses (Table 1).

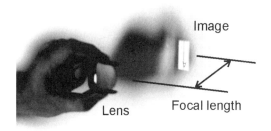

Object: for this example the letter A was taped on a fluorescent light fixture

Table 1: Focal lengths of lenses

	Focal length (mm)
White Lens	
Black lens	

Images can be smaller or larger than the object that created them. Images can also be right side up or inverted.

a. Was the image created by a single lens smaller or larger than the object?

b. Was the image right side up or was it inverted?

2 ▶ Projecting an image with a lens

You can think about a lens as collecting a cone of light from each point on an object.
For a perfect lens all the light in the cone is bent so it comes together at a point again to make the image. This is how movie projectors take an image on film and project it on a screen.

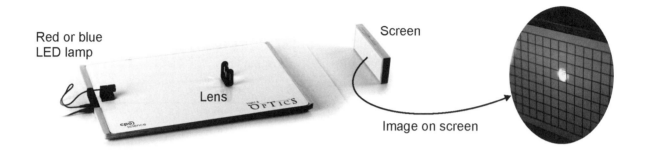

1. The red and blue LED lamps each have a letter F engraved on the front face. Take either color and place it near one edge of the optics table.

2. Take the white or black lens and set it on the optics table about 35 cm away from the LED lamp.

3. Take the screen and move it around until you can see a sharp image of the "F" on the screen.

4. Take a paper card and use it to block some of the light from the lens. The card should be 2-3 cm from the lens and on the same side as the LED lamp.

Observe the image on the screen as you *slowly* cover and uncover the lens.

3 ▶ Thinking about what you observed

a. Describe the characteristics of the image formed by the lens. Characteristics include whether the image right-side-up, inverted, larger, or smaller.

b. Discuss with your class why blocking part of the lens makes the image dimmer, even though you still see the entire image.

4 **Finding the magnification of a lens**

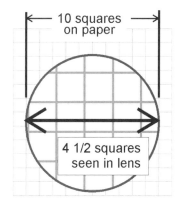

10 squares on paper

4 1/2 squares seen in lens

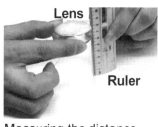

Measuring the distance from the lens to the paper

1. Take one of the lenses and set it on a piece of graph paper. Count the number of *unmagnified* squares that cross the diameter of the lens. In the example, the lens is 10 squares wide.

2. Look at the graph paper through the lens held above the paper at different distances. Move the lens until you have the biggest squares you can see clearly in the lens.

3. Count the number of *magnified* squares that cross the diameter of the lens. For example, the picture shows 4 1/2 squares across the lens.

4. The magnification is the number of *unmagnified* squares divided by the number of *magnified* squares. In the example, there are 10 *unmagnified* squares and 4.5 *magnified* squares. The magnification is 10 ÷ 4.5, or 2.22.

5. Try the experiment again using a ruler to measure the distance between the lens and the paper. Notice that the magnification changes with different distances.

Table 2: Magnification data for a single lens

Distance to paper (cm)	# of squares on the graph paper (unmagnified squares)	# of squares in the lens (magnified squares)	Magnification

 5 **Thinking about what you observed**

a. Is the image in a magnifying glass inverted or upright?

b. At what distances will the lens act like a magnifying glass? What happens when the object is more than a focal length away?

c. Describe something that looks completely different under a magnifying glass than when seen with the un-aided eye.

Optics and Images

Question for this Investigation:

How are images formed by light?

This Investigation will show you how some basic optical devices work. The technique is called geometric optics since it uses geometry to follow light rays through an optical system.

Materials

- Light and optics kit
- Room that may be darkened.
- Meter ruler
- Index card

1 ▲ The image in a mirror

1. Put a sheet of graph paper on the optics table and draw a line on the paper to mark where you will place a mirror.
2. Draw an arrow on the paper about 3 centimeters away from your line.
3. Place the reflecting surface of the mirror along the line and move your head until you can see the reflection of the arrow in the mirror.
4. Setup the laser and use the edge of a card to align the laser so the beam passes over the arrow's tip. Use the card to mark another spot on the beam. Use the marks to draw a line following the beam.
5. Use the card to points on the reflected laser beam then draw a line following the beam.
6. Move the laser so the beam passes over the arrow tip from a different angle but still hits the mirror. Draw the beam just as you did in steps 3 and 4.

Place the mirror on the paper where you drew the arrow so you can see the arrow in the mirror. The reflected rays create an image of the arrow that *appears* to come from behind the mirror. How does this happen?

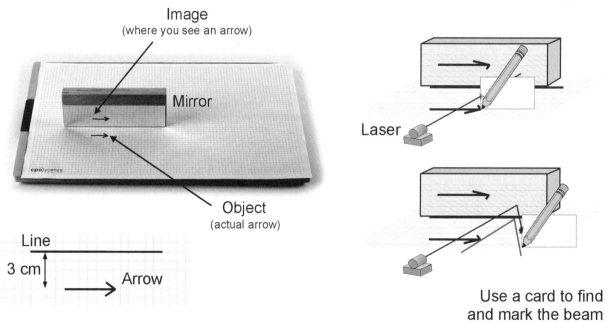

2 ▶ Thinking about what you observed

a. Relative to the mirror surface, where did the image of the arrow appear in the mirror? How deep into the mirror was the image?

b. Remove the mirror and use the ruler to extend the two reflected rays beyond where the mirror was. They should meet in a point on the other side of the line, like in the example on the right. What is the significance of the point where the reflected rays meet?

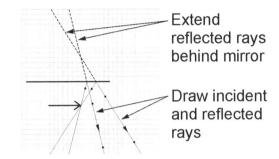

Extend reflected rays behind mirror

Draw incident and reflected rays

3 ▶ Refracting light through a lens

Lenses form images because they are able to bend light rays so they come to a point called the *focus*.

1. Fix a sheet of graph paper to the optics table with a magnetic strip.
2. Set the laser so it is tipped up on the magnetic strip. Align the laser so the beam follows a horizontal line across the paper.
3. Set the flat lens centered on the beam as shown in the diagram. Trace the shape of the lens on the graph paper.
4. Draw lines following the beam on both sides of the lens.
5. Move the laser to different parallel grid line above and below the center of the lens. Trace the beam on both sides of the lens for each position of the laser.

Align and mark beam   Beam splash (mark)

Laser

Flat lens

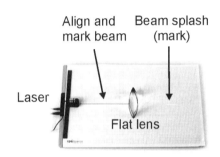

Move laser and align with a lower grid line

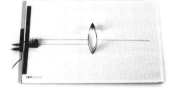

Move laser and align with an upper grid line

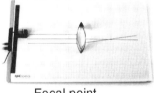

Focal point

Completed ray diagram

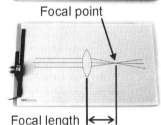

Focal length |←→|

4 ▶ Thinking about what you observed

a. Describe the path of the laser beam as it travels along the axis and through the lens.

b. What is the focal point of a lens? Mark the focal point on the ray diagram you just drew.

c. What is the focal length of a lens? Measure the focal length of the flat glass lens from the ray diagram.

d. Look back at your results from part 1 of Investigation 23A. Where does the image of a distant object form relative to the lens?

The Frequency and Wavelength of Light

Question for this Investigation:

How is the color of light related to its wavelength?

The wave properties of light are responsible for effects like the rainbow and the iridescent colors in soap bubbles. This Investigation will take a close look at the diffraction grating and use its properties to measure the wavelength of light.

Materials

- Light and optics kit
- Metric tape measure or ruler
- Light colored construction paper
- Colored pencils
- 2 Thumbtacks per group
- Spectrometer

1. Breaking light apart

Most of the light we see is made of a mixture of different colors. The diffraction grating glasses can separate the different colors. If you look at a bright light through the diffraction grating glasses, you see rainbows on all sides. Technically, the rainbows are called a *spectrum*. A spectrum shows what different colors of light make up a particular sample of light.

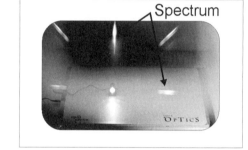

Sketch your observations of 1-5 with colored pencils in Table 1.

1. Look at the red LED through the diffraction glasses.
2. Look at the blue LED through the diffraction glasses.
3. Look at the green LED through the diffraction glasses.
4. Unscrew the color filter from one of the color LEDs. Look through the diffraction glasses at the light produced by the white LED and record your observations in the table.
5. Shine the red laser onto the screen. Look at the spot on the screen through the diffraction glasses.

Safety Note: DO NOT LOOK DIRECTLY AT THE LASER BEAM.

Table 1: Examining light sources

Red LED		Green LED		Blue LED
White LED			Red laser spot	

2 ▲ Thinking about what you observed

a. Describe the similarities and differences you observed in the spectra from the red, blue, and green LEDs.

b. Describe what you saw looking at the white LED. Compare the spectrum from the white LED with the spectra from red, green, and blue.

c. Describe the spectrum you saw looking through the diffraction grating glasses at the spot made by the red laser on the screen. How is the spectrum of the red laser different from the spectrum of the red LED?

d. Based on your observations, explain how the colored filters transform the white light of the LEDs inside the lamps into red, green, and blue.

3 ▲ The spectrometer

A *spectrometer* is an instrument that is designed around a diffraction grating. The spectrometer allows you to measure the wavelength of light of different colors.

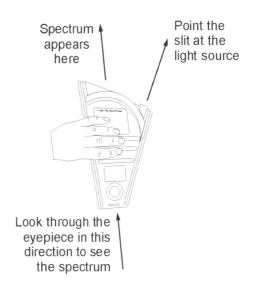

1. Use the spectrometer to look at red, green, and blue lights. Use Table 2 to record the range of wavelengths you see.

2. Shine the red laser on a white piece of paper. Look at the spot it makes with the spectrometer. Record the range of wavelengths you see.

3. Look at a fluorescent light bulb with the spectrometer. What range of wavelengths do you see? You will probably see two bright yellow lines in the spectrum from the fluorescent bulb. The yellow lines are the signature of the element mercury and come from the mercury vapor in the bulbs.

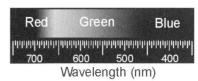

Wavelength (nm)

Table 2: Spectrometer observations

Apparent color	Observed range of wavelengths	Appearance of lines?

4 ▲ Thinking about what you observed

a. What range of wavelengths is visible light? Express your answer in meters.

b. Research the thickness of an average human hair. How many wavelengths of red laser light fit in the width of a hair?

c. Give a brief explanation of the colored lines in the spectrum of the fluorescent bulb.

123

Waves and Photons

Questions for this Investigation:

How do we know light has both wave-like and particle-like qualities?

Light acts like a transverse wave in many situations, with properties of frequency and wavelength. In other situations a beam of light acts like a stream of tiny energetic particles. This Investigation will show some experimental results that are best explained by thinking of light as a wave, and some that are best explained by thinking of light as streams of particles. Light has both wave-like and particle-like properties.

Materials

• Light and optics kit	• Room that may be darkened	• Slinky™ spring
• Foam cup & water	• Polarizing filters	• Waterproof marker

1 ▲ Polarization

A transverse wave on a spring can oscillate in two perpendicular directions: horizontal (side-to-side) or vertical (up-down).

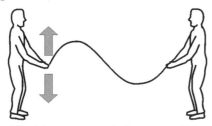

Shaking up-and-down makes
an up-and-down wave

Shaking side-to-side makes
a side-to-side wave

1. Find a partner. Each of you should take one end of the spring and stretch it. Do not let go or the spring will snap back suddenly.
2. One person should hold the spring firmly without moving. The other person should shake the spring up and down at the right frequency to get a wave (diagram) that oscillates up and down.
3. Shake the spring side to side at the same frequency until you get a wave that oscillates side-to-side.

2 ▲ Thinking about what you observed

a. Describe how the term *polarization* applies to the two different kinds of waves you made.

b. How many polarizations are there for a water wave like the one you made in Investigation 20A?

c. Suppose you shake the spring at an angle halfway between vertical and horizontal. This makes the wave also oscillate at the same angle. Is this angle a totally different kind of polarization or can it be represented as a combination of the other two waves you made before? You should discuss this question with your class because the answer is not simple.

The polarization of light

The two grey plastic squares in the optics kit are made of a special material called a _polarizer_. Some high-quality sunglasses are made of similar materials.

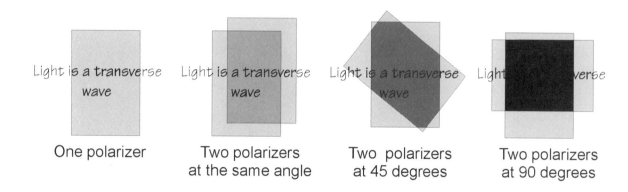

One polarizer

Two polarizers at the same angle

Two polarizers at 45 degrees

Two polarizers at 90 degrees

1. Take one sheet of polarizer and look through it. Observe the effect of looking through the polarizer. Try rotating the polarizer and see if it makes a difference.

2. Take a second sheet of polarizer and look through it. Observe the effects, just as with the first sheet.

3. Look through both sheets of polarizer together. Leave one fixed and rotate the other one as shown in the illustration above. Observe how much light you see through both polarizers as you rotate the second one.

 Thinking about what you observed

a. What is the difference between polarized and unpolarized light?

b. Why did the image appear the same when viewed through one polarizer, even when the polarizer was rotated to any angle?

c. Explain why rotating a second polarizer on top of the first polarizer changes the amount of light you see coming through. You may use the diagram below for reference.

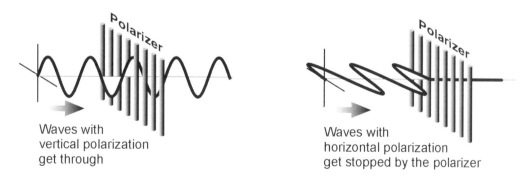

Waves with vertical polarization get through

Waves with horizontal polarization get stopped by the polarizer

d. Explain how polarization allows two waves to be different _even if they have the same frequency, amplitude, phase, and wavelength._

5 Reflecting on what you did

When we say that light is a wave, what exactly is waving? This is a difficult question.
When you push the north poles of two magnets together, they repel each other while some distance apart. The magnets feel force without touching because magnets create an *energy field* in the space around them. The energy field is what creates forces on other magnets. Electricity also creates an energy field. You may have felt this energy field in the air during a thunderstorm, or from static electricity on a dry day.

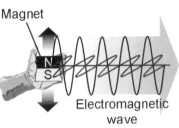
Magnet

Electromagnetic wave

The energy field created by electricity and magnetism can oscillate and it supports waves that move, just as water supports water waves. These waves are called electromagnetic waves, and light is one of them. Anything that creates an oscillation of electricity or magnetism creates electromagnetic waves. Moving a magnet up and down creates electromagnetic waves. If you could shake a magnet 450 trillion times per second, you would make waves of red light.

 6 Why polarizers make good sunglasses

1. Take a cup and draw some letters on the inside about 2 centimeters below the rim. Draw the letters with a waterproof permanent marker. Fill the the cup with water.

2. Place place the cup on a table (or the floor) a couple meters from a window. When you stand over the cup you can see the letters through the surface of the water.

3. Position yourself so you can see light from the window reflected of the surface of the water. The glare on the surface should prevent you from seeing the letters.

4. Look at the cup (and the glare) through a polarizer as you slowly rotate the polarizer. Notice you can see the letters sometimes, and sometimes you can't.

 7 Thinking about what you observed

a. Is there an orientation of the polarizer that allows you to see through the glare? If so, what is it?

b. What does this experiment tell you about the light that is reflected from the surface of the water compared to other light you see?

8 Glow-in-the-dark plastic

1. Uncover the greenish-white patch of glow-in-the-dark plastic (on the underside of the optics board) in a darkened room.

2. Cover part of the plastic with your hand or another opaque object. Expose the plastic to bright light for a few seconds.

3. Turn off the light source, remove the covering, and record your observations.

4. Expose the plastic to light completely uncovered.

5. Remove your hand and record your observations.

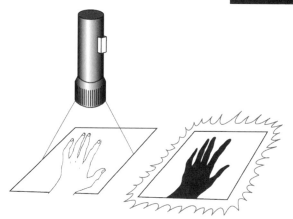

9 The effect of different colors

In this part you will test red, green, and blue light separately.

1. Allow the glow-in-the-dark material to stop glowing by leaving it in the dark for a few minutes.

2. Switch on the red LED lamp and shine it on the glow-in-the-dark material from a distance of about 10 centimeters. Wait 15 seconds and take the LED away and record your observations.

3. Try the same experiment again with the red LED 5 centimeters away and then again with the LED held right up against the surface. Decreasing the distance increases the intensity of the light without changing its color.

4. Repeat the procedure with the green LED. Record your observations.

5. Repeat the procedure with the blue LED. Record your observations.

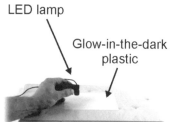

LED lamp

Glow-in-the-dark plastic

Underside of optics table

10 Thinking about what you observed

In answering these questions, think in terms of light and energy.

a. Why didn't the plastic that was covered by your hand glow? Explain in 1-2 sentences.

b. What is the energy of green light compared to red and blue?

c. Propose an explanation for why the red and blue lights had different effects on the glow-in-the-dark plastic.

d. Holding the LED lamp closer to the surface makes the light on the surface brighter. Brighter light means more energy. The red light did not make a glow even when it was close, while the blue light made a glow even 10 cm away. How does the photon theory of light explain this observation? This is a class discussion question and the answer took many years to deduce.

Physics Stand

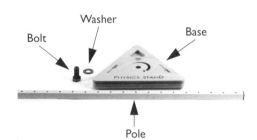

1. Identifying the parts of the physics stand.

There are four parts to the physics stand; the base, the pole, the washer and the bolt.

2. Placing the bolt into the base.

From the bottom of the base slide the large bolt through the hole.

3. Sliding the washer onto the bolt.

Be sure to push the bolt into the cut-out triangle on the bottom of the stand. The washer will fit over the threaded part of the bolt.

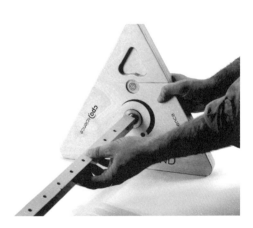

4. Attaching the pole to the base.

The pole screws onto the threads of the bolt. The bolt will not spin when you hold the bolt into the cut-out triangle on the bottom of the base. Spin the pole until it screws down snug onto the washer.

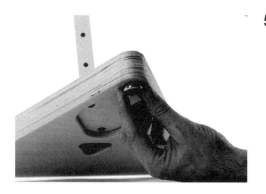

5. **Leveling the stand.**

There are three adjustable feet on the bottom of the base. These feet screw into the base. They can be extended by unscrewing them a few turns.

Bubble

6. **Using the leveling bubble.**

When the bubble is directly in the center of the small circle, the stand is level. By adjusting the feet on the bottom of the base by small amounts, the stand can be brought into level.

Energy Car

You will need:

- 2 sections of track
- Rubber bands
- Some string
- A small bubble level

- Three blue knobs
- 2 Cars
- Some modeling clay
- 3 steel balls (3/4" dia.)

- 2 Stops
- 1 Sled
- Physics Stand

Track sections (2)

Knobs (3)

Stops (2)

Sled   Cars (2)

Steel balls (3)

1. Parts of the car and track.

You will also need some rubber bands. #33 rubber bands work well but other sizes will also work. A small ball of modeling clay about 2 cm in diameter is also necessary.

The Sled is the same as the Car, but without wheels.

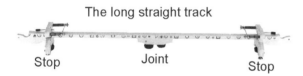

The long straight track

Stop   Joint   Stop

2. Setting up the long straight track

The long straight track is used for many experiments.

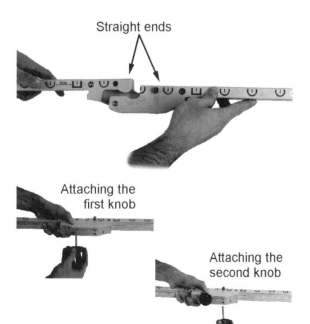

Straight ends

Attaching the first knob

Attaching the second knob

3. Joining the track sections

The two sections of the track join together with two blue knobs.

Notice that the ends of the track sections are different. One end is straight and the other has a slight curve. Join the two straight ends together to make the long straight track. The curved ends are for making a hill.

Screw one blue knob into each of the two holes on the bottom of the joint where the two track sections meet.

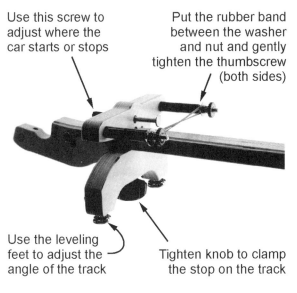

Use this screw to adjust where the car starts or stops

Put the rubber band between the washer and nut and gently tighten the thumbscrew (both sides)

Use the leveling feet to adjust the angle of the track

Tighten knob to clamp the stop on the track

4. Attaching the stop and making a car launcher

The stop is used to both start and stop the car on the track. There are two stops, one for each end. They are identical.

To make the stop into a launcher, loosen the two thumbscrews by a few turns. Stretch a rubber band between the two screws. The rubber band should fit behind the washer. Give the rubber band one twist so it makes an "X" between the posts. The X helps provide even force when launching the car.

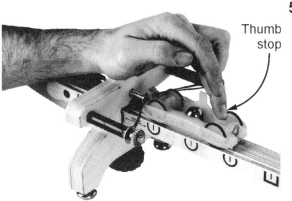

Thumb stop

5. Launching the car

To launch the car, rest your hand on the top of the launcher and catch the thumb stop on the car with your finger (diagram).

Pull the car back until it hits the screw. Change the adjustment of the screw to get different speeds.

Flick your finger back and off the thumb stop with a quick motion to launch the car. With practice you can get speeds that are repeatable to within 1%.

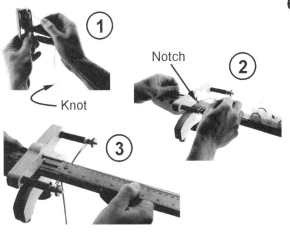

① ② ③ ④

Notch

Knot

6. Measuring the force on the car

(1) Tie a knot on the end of a length of string. Thread the string through the small hole in the end of the car so the knot is on top the car.

(2) Thread the string through the notch just below the screw on the wooden stop. Tie a small loop on the free end of the string about 20 cm away from the wooden stop.

(3) Use a ruler to set the distance from the front of the screw to the front of the rubber band. Distances from 1 cm to 5 cm can be obtained.

(4) Attach a force scale to the loop on the string and pull the car back until it just touches the screw. The scale reads the force on the car at the measured deflection of the rubber band.

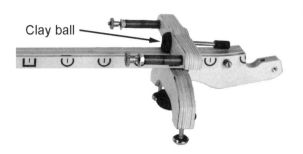

Clay ball

7. Stopping the car

Squish a small ball of modeling clay on the end of the screw to make a stop for the car. The clay prevents the car from bouncing.

Adjust the leveling feet on one or both ends until the bubble is exactly centered

8. Leveling the track

Some experiments require that the track be level. A small bubble-level works very well for this purpose. Adjust the leveling feet until the bubble is exactly in the center between the marking lines on the level.

Attaching the photogate

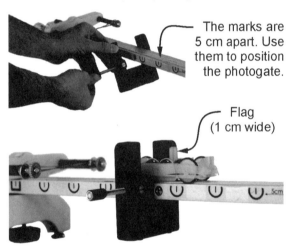

The marks are 5 cm apart. Use them to position the photogate.

Flag (1 cm wide)

9. Using the photogates

The car has a small flag on top that breaks the light beam in the photogates. The flag is one centimeter wide.

Attach photogates as shown in the diagram. The flag breaks the light beam when the photogate is snug against the bottom of the track.

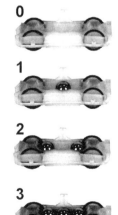

Add mass to the car so the steel balls are evenly spaced around the center of the car,

0

1

2

3

10. Adding mass to the car

The steel ball add mass to the car. Each ball is 50% of the mass of the empty car. That means adding one ball increases the mass by 50%. Adding two balls doubles the mass.

The car is designed so the center of mass stays in the same place if the balls are added symmetrically around the center (diagram).

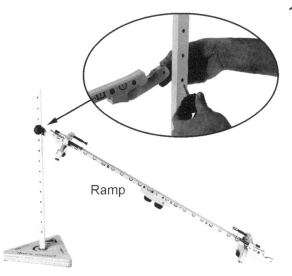

Ramp

11. Making a straight ramp

The long straight track can be attached to the Physics Stand to make a ramp. Insert a blue knob through a hole in the stand and screw the threaded end into the end of the ramp.

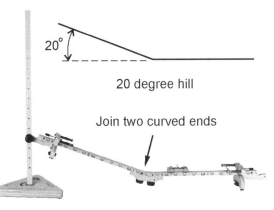

20°

20 degree hill

Join two curved ends

12. Making a flat section with a hill

You can join the two sections of the track to make a 10 degree hill or a 20 degree hill. To make the 10 degree hill join one curved end to one straight end. To make a 20 degree hill joining both curved ends together.

Use the Physics Stand to support the track at the top of the hill.

hole

Knot

(1)

(2)

13. Measuring height on the hill

A level string can be used as a reference to measure the height of the car on the hill.

(1) Make the horizontal section of the track level. Tie a knot in one end of a string and thread the string through the small hole in the stop.

(2) Use a photogate and a knob to clamp the other end of the string against the Physics Stand. Adjust the position until the string is parallel to the horizontal section of the track.

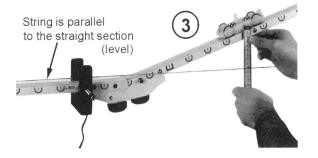

String is parallel to the straight section (level)

(3)

The string is now level and at the same height as the center of mass of the car! You can easily make height measurements on the hill by measuring the vertical distance between the center of the car and the string.

Steel balls go here

Runners slide on the track

14. Using the sled

The sled is just like the car, but without wheels. The sled is used for friction experiments.

Ropes and Pulleys

You will need:

- Physics stand assembly
- 1 set of weights
- Tape measure

- Upper and lower pulley blocks attached by red safety string
- 1 set of spring scales
- Blue knob

- Yellow string with cord stops
- Black knob

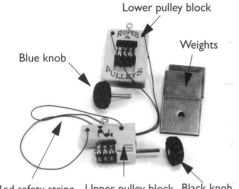

Lower pulley block

Weights

Blue knob

Red safety string   Upper pulley block   Black knob

1. **Identifying the parts of the ropes and pulleys.**

The ropes and pulleys set is an ideal way to learn the basic principles behind how simple machines work. The upper and lower pulley blocks each contain three pulleys. The number of pulleys through which the string passes can be varied by passing the string through the desired number. The force of the bottom pulley block can be varied by adding or subtracting weights. The pulleys contain low friction bearings for accurate force measurements.

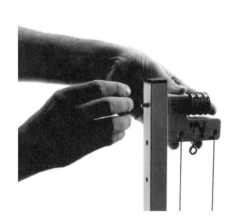

2. **Attaching the upper pulley block.**

Slide the threaded rod attached to the upper pulley block through the top hole of the physics stand. Secure the pulley block with the black knob. You should now have the upper pulley block secured, while the lower pulley block hangs below on the two red safety strings.

3. **Weighing the bottom block.**

Add weights to the bottom block using the blue knob with the threaded stud. Slide the threaded stud through the hole in the weight and screw it into the bottom of the lower pulley.

After the weights have been secured, weigh the lower pulley block by hanging it onto a spring scale using the eyelet on top.

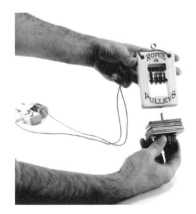

4.

Stringing the pulley blocks.

The yellow string is the one you will use to move the lower pulley block up and down. The red strings are the safety strings that hold the bottom block while you arrange the yellow strings. The cord stops are used as reference markers for measuring the length of string needed to raise the lower block a given distance.

The first step to stringing the ropes & pulleys is to choose where to connect the brass clip on the end of the yellow string. The clip can either be attached to the upper pulley block or the lower pulley block using the eyelet on either block.

Connect string to the lower pulley block for mechanical advantage of 1,3, or 5.

If the string is connected to the lower pulley block a mechanical advantage of 1, 3 or 5 can be obtained (1, 3, or 5 supporting strings). The diagram to the right shows a mechanical advantage of 1.

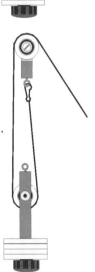

If the string is connected to the upper pulley block a mechanical advantage of 2, 4, or 6 can be obtained (2, 4, or 6 supporting strings). The diagram to the right shows a mechanical advantage of 2.

Connect string to the upper pulley block for mechanical advantage of 2,4, or 6.

Marble Launcher

You will need:

- Marble launcher
- Black plastic marble
- 2 Hex screws
- Hex wrench

1. **Identifying the parts of the marble launcher.**

The marble launcher will come with six pieces; the base, the main assembly, a small black marble, two small hex nuts, and a small hex wrench.

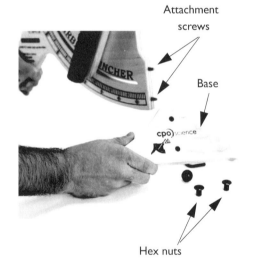

Attachment screws

Base

Hex nuts

2. **Setting up the marble launcher.**

The marble launcher itself has two parts; the base and the main assembly. These two parts attach together with hex nuts that fit onto attachment screws that are embedded into the bottom of the main assembly. Line up the two holes in the base with the attachment screws on the main assembly.

Hex wrench

3. **Attaching the base.**

The hex nuts fit onto the attachment screws through the holes in the base. Use the small hex wrench to tighten both until snug.

4.   **Loading the marble.**

Set launcher to desired angle before loading the marble. To load, put the marble right into the hole at the top of the barrel. **Be sure to load the marble into the barrel before pulling the launch lever back into the locked and ready to fire position.**

5.   **Launching the marble.**

Launch lever

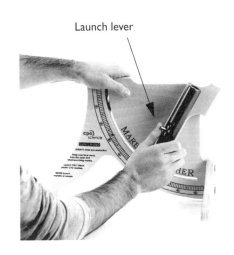

After loading the marble into the barrel pull the launch lever back to one of the five possible notches and set into place. The marble launcher will be ready to launch. Push down on the launch lever gently with your thumb to slowly slide the lever off the notch to send the marble flying.

Atom Building Game

You will need:

- Atom game board
- 1 tube yellow marbles
- Laminated periodic table
- 1 tube blue marbles
- Nuclear Reactions cards
- Game booklet
- 1 tube red marbles
- Photons and Lasers cards

1. Identifying the parts of the game.

The Atom Building Game comes with an atom game board, blue, red, and yellow marbles, game cards, a laminated periodic table, and an instruction booklet.

The game cards include Nuclear Reactions cards and Photons and Lasers cards. You will learn how to use these cards in the Investigations.

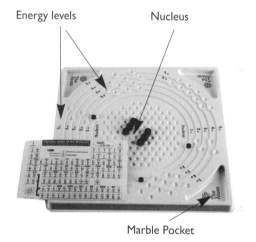

Energy levels   Nucleus

Marble Pocket

2. Using the atom game board.

The Atom game board is designed to sit on a table top with four players (or teams) around it. Each player (or team) is assigned to one of the four marble pockets.

The center of the board represents the nucleus. This is where the protons (red marbles) and neutrons (blue marbles) are place during the activities.

The steps around the nucleus represent the energy levels that are occupied by the electrons (yellow marbles).

3. Using the periodic table.

The periodic table is used for many of the activities. The atomic number is the number of protons (red marbles) in the nucleus.

The atomic number determines what element the atom is. The mass number is the total number of particles (protons plus neutrons) in the nucleus.

Isotopes are atoms with the same number of protons but different numbers of neutrons. You can figure out the number of neutrons by subtracting the atomic number from the mass number. For example, lithium-6 has 3 protons and 3 neutrons (6 - 3 = 3).

Neutral atoms have the same number of electrons as protons. The atom in step 2 is lithium-6.

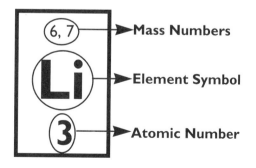

(6, 7) ➤ **Mass Numbers**

Li ➤ **Element Symbol**

(3) ➤ **Atomic Number**

Electric Circuits

You will need:

- Electric circuits table
- 6 light bulbs and 3 holders
- 2 brown (long-length) wires
- 1 red (20-ohm) resistor

- 1 potentiometer
- 6 green (short-length) wires
- 2 green (5-ohm) resistors
- 2 knife switches

- 2 battery holders
- 2 blue (medium-length) wires
- 1 blue (10-ohm) resistor

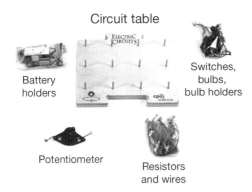

Circuit table

Battery holders

Switches, bulbs, bulb holders

Potentiometer

Resistors and wires

1.   **Identifying the parts of the electric circuits kit.**

The electric circuits table is a wooden platform with brass posts for securely assembling electric circuits. There are 12 brass posts used in making connections between different components of the circuit

The posts are not connected underneath and there are no hidden wires. All connections are made using wires that come in a separate pack.

Circuits are made with wires, batteries, bulbs and holders, resistors, and switches.

2.   **Assembling the components.**

Place D batteries (1.5 volts) into the battery holders.

Place a light bulb into each bulb holder.

3. Adding wires and circuit elements.

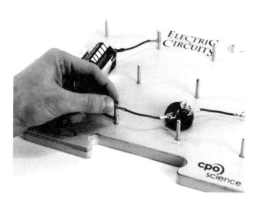

Each wire has a circular connector at both ends called a hoop connector. To add a wire to the board, just place the hoop around the post and push down on the hoop. It will slide down the post, like a jewelry ring over a finger. If you need to add one or more wires to the post, simply push the first wire down the post to make room for another hoop. You can add up to 4 hoops to a post.

NOTE: Solid contact is made at any position on the post. It is not necessary to slide every wire to the bottom of the post.

A circuit element is any item that uses or affects electricity in a circuit. This includes batteries, light bulbs, resistors and switches. Each circuit element that comes with the kit has the same type of hoop connectors as the wires. To connect a circuit element to a post just place the hoop on the post and push down, sliding it down the post.

4. Closing the circuit.

A circuit is made when wires and elements are connected together making a path for electricity. Shown at left is an example of a simple circuit with a battery, a light bulb, a switch, and some wires.

5. Avoiding short circuits.

Circuits should always include a "resistor." The term "resistor" refers to a device like a light bulb or one of the resistors that comes with the kit and provides a substantial resistance to the flow of electricity. A wire alone in a circuit provides very little resistance and is not considered a resistor. A circuit without a resistor, or one in which a branch bypasses a resistor, is called a short circuit. A *short circuit* causes unsafe heating of connecting wires, batteries, and battery holders. This could result in burns and irreparable damage to the equipment. Avoid short circuits at all times!

Ripcord Generator

You will need:

- Base/rotor assembly
- Ripcord
- Electromagnet coil
- Steel pin
- Electric circuit board

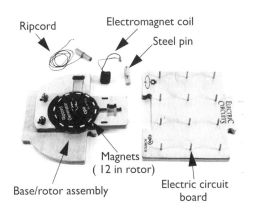

Ripcord
Electromagnet coil
Steel pin
Magnets (12 in rotor)
Base/rotor assembly
Electric circuit board

1.   **Identifying the parts of the ripcord generator.**

The ripcord generator is used with the Electric Circuit board, as pictured here. The parts of the ripcord generator include the base/rotor assembly, the ripcord, the electromagnet coil, twelve magnets, and the steel pin.

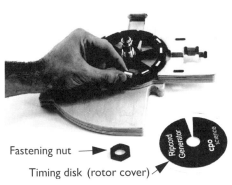

Fastening nut
Timing disk (rotor cover)

2.   **Inserting the magnets.**

Depending on the activity, up to twelve magnets can be placed into the pockets on the rotor. Be sure to check the orientation of the magnets when you place them into the rotor. Two other parts of the ripcord generator are pictured here; the fastening nut and the timing disk (rotor cover).

3.   **Attaching the timing disk (rotor cover).**

The timing disk fits over the spindle of the rotor. The side of the disk with the writing and graphics on it should face upwards.

4.   **Screwing the fastening nut onto the spindle.**

Screw the fastening nut onto the spindle until snug.

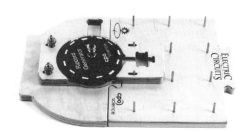

5. Attaching the generator to the circuit board.

The ripcord generator and the circuit board have sides that fit together like a puzzle.

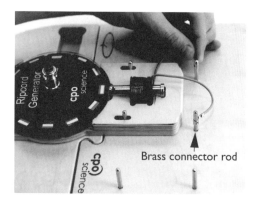

Brass connector rod

6. Attaching the electromagnet coil.

There is a cut-out hole on the base of the rotor assembly that the electromagnet coil will fit right into. Drop the electromagnet coil into the cut-out hole and slide the wires from the coil over the connector rods on the electric circuit board. There are small metal hoops on the end of the wires that fit perfectly right over the connector rods.

7. Attaching the rip cord using the knot.

There is a knot on the end of the ripcord. Wrap the string around the spindle so the knot on the string fits into the hole on the spindle.

8. Wrapping the string onto the spindle.

Continue wrapping the string around the spindle. Wind the string around the narrow part of the spindle.

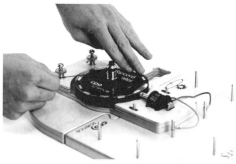

9. Winding the string around the spindle.

Once the string has become securely attached to the spindle, use the timing disk (rotor cover) to quickly wind the rest of the string around. Leave about four to five inches of string toward the handle as you wind the string to give yourself enough room to pull the ripcord.

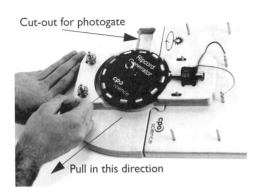

Cut-out for photogate

Pull in this direction

10. **Pulling the rip cord.**

Grab the handle securely with one hand, allowing the string to fit in between your fingers (do not wrap string around your fingers). Hold the base of the generator assembly firmly. Pull the ripcord with a straight motion, pulling directly away from the spindle.

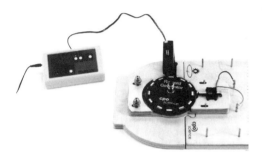

11. **Attaching a photogate and Timer.**

One photogate will fit down into the cut-out hole on the side of the rotor. Connect one end of a phone cord to the photogate once it is securely in place. Connect the other end of the phone cord to the Timer into the slot marked "A". Attach the adapter cord to the Timer for power and then plug it into a wall socket. Turn the Timer on and use the mode switch to set the Timer to Frequency.

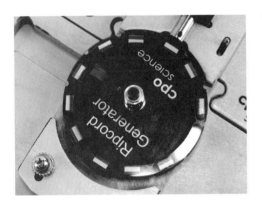

12. **Positioning the timing disk (rotor cover).**

Once the disk is on the spindle and snug in place with the attachment nut, be sure to position the disk so that the clear wedge is **not** positioned over one of the spokes of the rotor. By loosening the fastening nut slightly and holding the rotor in place, you can turn the disk so no spokes are blocking the clear wedge. Once the wedge is properly positioned, tighten the fastening nut snug onto the disk.

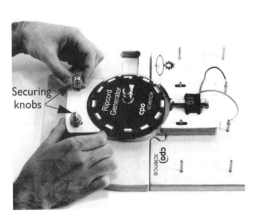

Securing knobs

13. **Adjusting the rotor to coil distance.**

The distance between the rotor and the coil can be adjusted by loosening both securing knobs on the base/rotor assembly. Once the securing knobs are loosened, the part of the base/rotor assembly that holds the electromagnet coil can slide back and forth, allowing for the rotor to electromagnet coil distance to be adjusted.

Pendulum

You will need:

- Physics stand assembly
- Pendulum bob and string assembly
- Pendulum face
- 10 washers
- 2 blue knobs with threaded stud
- Timer and photogates

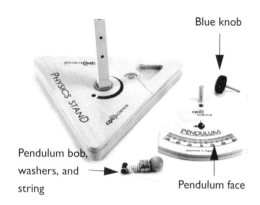

Blue knob

Pendulum bob, washers, and string

Pendulum face

1. Identifying the parts of the pendulum.

The pendulum experiment allows you to change three variables: the length of the string, the mass of the pendulum, and the angle of the swing (amplitude). The length of the string can be varied from 15 cm to nearly 1 meter. The pendulum has a hardwood face with an angle scale for easy determination of the amplitude. Washers can be added to or subtracted from the pendulum bob to change the mass.

2. Attaching the pendulum face to the physics stand.

Slide the threaded stud on the blue knob through the desired hole in the physics stand.

Turn the blue knob to thread the stud into the back of the pendulum face, securing it to the physics stand.

3. Attaching the pendulum bob and string

Select the length of string for the pendulum bob by sliding the string into the slot in the peg on the pendulum face. Check the length of the string by measuring from the bottom of the slotted peg to the bottom of the stack of washers on the pendulum bob. You can add or subtract washers from the pendulum bob to change the mass.

4.   Mounting the photogate to the physics stand.

To mount the photogate to the physics stand, you will need another blue knob with threaded stud. Place the outer edge of the photogate to against the hole that allows you to align the opening with the pendulum bob. Do not overtighten. Make sure the pendulum bob breaks the beam in the photogate each time it swings.

5.   Aligning the photogate

Be sure to align the two small holes in the photogate with the center of the round portion of the pendulum bob.

Attach the photogate to slot A in the timer using the red or blue wire. Be sure the "A" light is on and that the timer is set to period mode.

Sound and Waves

You will need:

- Physics stand assembly
- Sound & waves console
- Elastic string

- Wiggler
- Blue or red phone cord
- 2 black knobs

- Fiddlehead
- Black phono wire
- Timer

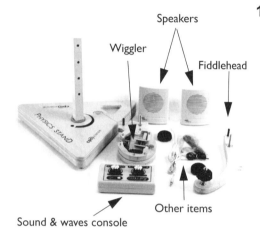

Speakers

Wiggler

Fiddlehead

Sound & waves console

Other items

1.

Identifying the parts of the kit.

The sound and waves kit contains a wiggler for creating standing waves on a string and a sound synthesizer that can make pure tones at frequencies ranging from 20 to 25,000 hertz. The components in the kit are shown at the right.

2.

Attaching the wiggler and fiddlehead.

Attach the wiggler by placing the two threads through the bottom two holes on the physics stand. Secure the wiggler with a black knob.

Attach the fiddlehead by placing the threaded rod and peg on the head through the top two holes on the physics stand. Secure with another black knob. Be sure the black knobs for each piece are on the same side of the physics stand pole. The top of the fiddlehead will be higher than the physics stand pole when it is attached.

3.

Attach the string to the wiggler and fiddlehead.

The wiggler arm is a narrow metal strip shaped like an arrow. The tip of the wiggler arm protrudes from the wiggler about 2 cm. If the string is not already attached to the wiggler, locate the hole in the wiggler arm and thread the elastic string through the hole. Knot the string at the end. This knot will create a stop so that the string can be pulled tight.

Attach the free end of the string to the fiddlehead by pulling it to the top knob on the fiddlehead. At this point there should be no slack in the string. Now tighten the string by stretching it a little (5-10 cm). Then, wrap the end around the back of the knob - sliding it between two of the washers. Lightly tighten the black plastic knob, securing the string between the washers.

4.

Connect the sound and waves console.

Connect the black phono wire into the bottom of the wiggler. Connect the other end of the black phono wire into the round jack on the sound and waves console.

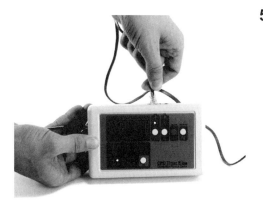

5. **Connecting to the timer.**

Turn on the timer and set to *frequency* mode. Plug one end of the phone cord into the **A** slot on the timer and the other end into the square jack in on sound and waves console. Make sure that the **A** light is illuminated on the timer.

Set the sound and waves console to *waves* mode by pushing the button to illuminate the *waves* light.

Change the frequency on the sound and waves console by turning the frequency knob left or right.

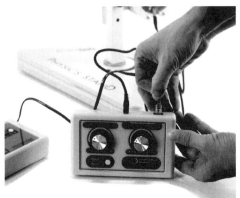

6. **Using the sound mode.**

Unplug the black phono wire from the sound and waves console and connect the end of the wire from the speakers into the round jack.

Set the sound and waves console to *sound* mode by pressing the button until the *sound* light is illuminated.

Connect the sound and waves console to the timer using the square jack and set the timer to *frequency* mode.

Adjust the frequency by turning the frequency knob. Adjust the volume by turning the volume knob.

Light and Optics

You will need:

- Optics table
- LED lamps
- Diffraction grating glasses
- Magnet securing strips

- Power adapter
- Laser
- Polarizing filters
- Large graph paper

- Flat lenses
- Prism
- Mirror/projection screen

1. Parts of the Light & Optics kit.

The lights & optics kit comes with the optics table, a power adapter, three flat lenses, three LED lamps (red, green and blue), a red laser, a prism, diffraction grating glasses, two polarizing filters, a mirror/projection screen, two magnetic securing strips, and large graph paper.

LED lamps and laser jacks (4)

Power adapter jack

2. Attaching the adapter to the optics table.

On the side of the optics table there is a series of jacks. Four of them are identical and are used to plug in the LED lights and the laser. One if them is not like the others and it is on the far right of the black plastic plate. Plug the power adapter into this jack, and then plug the other end into a wall outlet.

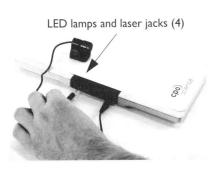

LED lamps and laser jacks (4)

3. Attaching the LED lamps to the optics table.

There are four identical jacks on the side of the optics table. You can use any one of these jacks for all three LED lamps or the laser. Plug in one of the lamps to make sure your optics table has power. There is no on/off switch, the light should go on if there is power.

Glow in the dark material.

Underside of table

4. Finding the glow in the dark sticker.

On the underside of the optics table there is sticker made out of glow in the dark material. It can be made to glow by exposing it to light, and can be observed to glow in a darkened room.

Using Computer Spreadsheets

Computer spreadsheets provide an easy way to organize and evaluate data that you collect from an experiment. Numbers are typed into boxes called "cells." The cells are organized in rows and columns. You can find the average of a lot of numbers or do more complicated calculations by writing formulas into the cells. Each cell has a name based on its column letter and row number. For example, the first cell in most spreadsheets is "A1."

By the end of this project you will have experience doing the following tasks:

	A	B	C	D	
1	Time (sec)	Temp (deg C)	Slope		
2	0	22.5			
3	30	23.0			
4	60	23.5			
5	90	24.0			
6	120	25.5			
7	150	27.5			
8	180	30.0			
9	210	32.5			
10	240	35.0			
11	270	37.5			
12	300	40.0			
13					
14					
15					

1. Recording data in a computer spreadsheet program.

2. Doing simple calculations for many data values at once using the spreadsheet.

3. Making a graph with the data set.

MATERIALS

- Simple calculator
- Access to a computer with a spreadsheet program

DIRECTIONS ▶

1. **Adding data:** Open the spreadsheet program on your computer. You will see a window open that has rows and columns. The rows are numbered. The columns are identified by a letter.

    a. As shown in the graphic above, add headings for columns A, B, and C:
    cell A1, type "Time (sec)"
    cell B1, type "Temp (deg C)"
    cell C1, type "Slope"
    NOTE: You can change the width of the columns on your spreadsheet by clicking on the right-hand border and dragging the border to the left or right.

    b. Highlight column B. Then, go to the **Format** menu item and click on **Cells**. Make the format of these cells **Number** with one decimal place. Highlight column C and make the format of these cells Number with two decimal places.

    c. Type in the data for Time and Temperature as shown in the graphic above.

2. **Making a graph:** Now, you will use the data you have added to the skill sheet to make a graph.

    a. Use your mouse to highlight the titles and data in columns A and B.

    b. Then, go to **Insert** and click on **Chart**.

    c. In step 1 of the chart wizard, choose the **XY (Scatter)** format for your chart and click "Next."

    d. In step 2 of the chart wizard, you will see a graph of your data. Click "Next" again to get to step 3. Here, you can change the appearance of the graph.

e. In step 3 of the chart wizard add titles and uncheck the show legend-option. In the box for the chart title write "Temperature vs. Time." In the box for the value x-axis, write "Time (seconds)." In the box for the value for y-axis, write "Temperature (deg Celsius)."

f. In step 4 of the chart wizard, click the option to show the graph as an object in Sheet 2. At this point you will finish your work with the chart wizard.

g. Setting the scale on the x-axis. Place the cursor on the x-axis and double click. Set the minimum of the scale to be 0, the maximum to be 310. Set the major unit to be 100 and the minor unit to be 20. Then, click OK. *Note: Make sure the boxes to the left of the changed values are NOT checked.*

h. Setting the scale on the y-axis. Place the cursor on the y-axis and double click. Set the minimum of the scale to be 20, the maximum to be 41. Set the major unit to be 10 and the minor unit to be 2. Then, click OK. *Note: Make sure the boxes to the left of the changed values are UNchecked.*

i. You are now finished with your graph. It is located on Sheet 2 of your spreadsheet.

3. **Performing calculations:**

a. Return to Sheet 1 of your spreadsheet.

b. The third column of data, "Slope," will be filled by performing a calculation using data in the other two columns.

c. Highlight the second cell from the top in the Slope column (cell C2). Type the following and hit enter:
= (B3-B2)/(A3-A2)
Explanation of the formula: The equal sign (=) indicates that the information you type into the cell is a formula. The formula for the slope of a line is as follows. Do you see why the formula for cell C2 is written the way it is?

$$\text{slope} = \frac{y_2 - y_1}{x_2 - x_1}$$

d. Adding the formula to all the cells: Highlight cell C2, then drag the mouse down the column until the cells (C2 to C11) are highlighted. Then click **Edit**, then **Fill**, then **Down**. The formula will copy into each cell in column C. However, the formula pattern will be appropriate for each cell. For example, the formula for C2 reads: = (B3-B2)/(A3-A2). The formula for C3 reads: = (B4-B3)/(A4-A3). Note: The "=" sign is important. Do not forget to add it to the formula.

e. In column C, you will see the slope for pairs of data points. Now, answer the questions below.

QUESTIONS ?

a. Which is the independent variable—time or temperature? Which is the dependent variable?

b. When setting up the data in a spreadsheet, which data set goes in the first column, the independent variable or the dependent variable?

c. Use the graph you created in step 2 of the directions to describe the relationship between temperature and the time it takes to heat up a volume of water.

d. Look at the values for slope. How do these values change for the graph of temperature versus time?

PRACTICE

a. The following data is from an experiment in which the temperature of a substance was taken as it was heated. Transfer this data into an Excel file and make an XY(Scatter) graph.

Time (seconds) Independent data	Temperature (°C) Dependent data
10	7.5
20	10.8
30	11.6
40	11.9
50	13.3
60	21.9
70	26.3
80	26.6
90	29.1
100	31.1

b. Use the following data set to make a graph in Excel. Find the slope for pairs of data points along the plot of the graph. Is the slope the same for every pair of points?

Independent data	Dependent data
1	5
2	7
2.5	8
3.2	9.4
1.5	6
0.5	4
4	11
2.8	8.6
4.2	11.4
5	13

Calculating Bicycle Gear Ratios

How many gears does your bicycle really have?

Bicycle manufacturers describe any bicycle with two gears in the front and five in the back as a ten-speed. But do you really get ten different speeds? In this project, you will determine and record the gear ratio for each speed of your bicycle. You will then write up an explanation of the importance (or lack of, in some cases) of each speed. You will explain what the rider experiences due to the physics of the gear ratio, and in what situation the rider would take advantage of that particular speed.

MATERIALS

- Multi-speed bicycle
- Simple calculator
- Access to a library or the Internet for research
- Access to a computer for work with a spreadsheet (optional)

DIRECTIONS ▶

1. On a multi-speed bicycle, there are two groups of gears: the front group and the rear group. You may want to carefully place your bicycle upside down on the floor to better work with the gears. The seat and handlebars will keep the bicycle balanced.

2. Draw a schematic diagram to show how the gears are set up on your bicycle.

3. Now, count the number of teeth on each gear in each group. Record your data in a table on paper or in a computer spreadsheet. Use these questions to guide you.

   a. How many gears are in the front group?

   b. How many teeth on each gear in the front group?

   c. How many gears are in the rear group?

   d. How many teeth on each gear in the rear group?

4. Now, calculate the gear ratio for each front/rear combination of gears.
    Use the formula: front gear ÷ rear gear.
    Organize the results of your calculations into a new table either on paper on in a computer spreadsheet.
    How many different gear ratios do you actually have?

5. Use your library or the Internet to research the development of the multi-speed bicycle. Take careful notes while you do your research as you will use the information you find to write a report (see step 7). In your research, find the answers to the following questions.

    a. In what circumstances would a low gear ratio be helpful? Why?

    b. In what circumstances would a high gear ratio be helpful? Why?

6. Write up your findings and results according to the guidelines below.

Your final project should include:

• **A brief (one page) report** that discusses the evolution of the bicycle. What was the first bicycle like? How did we end up with the modern bicycle? Why was the multi-speed bicycle and important invention?

• **A schematic diagram** of your bicycle's gears. Include labels.

• **An organized, professional data table** showing the gear ratios of your bicycle.

• **A summary report** (one page) in which you interpret your findings and explain the trade-off between force and distance when pedaling a bicycle in each of the different speeds. Include answers to questions 5(a) and 5(b). In your research, you should make a surprising discovery about the speeds—what is it?

• **Reflection:** Finish the report with one or two paragraphs that express your reflections on this project.

Measuring Surface Tension

Working in her own kitchen in northern Germany, nineteenth century self-taught scientist Agnes Pockels invented new methods of studying the surface tension of water and other liquids. **Surface tension** *refers to the attraction that molecules in a liquid have for each other at the surface of the liquid. The property of surface tension explains why water "beads up" on a newly waxed car, and why the water strider, a common insect, can walk on the surface of water.*

Pockels wrote a letter to a famous British scientist, Lord Raleigh, about her work on surface tension. He was so impressed that he had the letter translated into English and published in the journal Nature. You can make your own "button balance" like the one Agnes Pockels used.

MATERIALS ☑

- Plastic ruler with holes (see diagram)
- Nylon thread or fishing line (works well because it doesn't absorb water)
- Small plastic button with a rim on one side
- Cone-style coffee filter to use as a counterbalance pan
- A small plastic container filled with water (such as a quart-sized bowl)
- Clear tape
- Small weights (try plastic beads, small paper clips, sand, squares of graph paper, etc.)
- Tweezers
- Simple calculator and/or access to a simple computer and spreadsheet program.

DIRECTIONS ▶

1. Set up the balance as shown in the diagram. Try substituting materials you have around the house if you do not have a coffee filter, ruler, or other item in the list.

2. Hang the balance from a cupboard or doorknob. Or, invent your own balance stand. Make sure the balance is level before you start. If necessary, add a bit of tape to one side to even things out.

3. Next, raise your water container so that the button (rim downwards) settles gently onto the liquid's surface. You should notice the lever tip towards the liquid.

4. Add small weights to your counterbalance pan until the button separates from the water.

5. Record the amount of weight you needed to remove the button from the liquid surface.

6. Try repeating your experiment to see how close together the measurements are. If your results vary a lot, make sure that it is the weight itself, rather than the act of placing it in the counterbalance pan, that is causing the button to separate from the liquid. Try to put the button back on the liquid. If it stays, you haven't used enough weight yet. Try adding the weights with tweezers rather than dropping them in the pan.

155

ACTIVITIES ✋

After you are satisfied that your balance is producing reliable results, choose one of these activities:

1. Demonstrate your balance for the class. Describe any design changes that you incorporated to improve its performance.

2. Compare the surface tension of tap water to that of salt water. Be sure to consider which variables you will need to control to make your comparison valid.

3. Agnes Pockels wondered if the same amount of weight would be required to remove the button from a small surface area of water and a large surface area. In order to test this, she made a special container. She describes it in her letter to Lord Rayleigh:

    "A rectangular tin trough, 70 cm. long, 5 cm. wide, 2 cm. high, is filled with water to the brim, and a strip of tin about 1 1/2 cm. laid across it perpendicular to its length, so that the underside of the strip is in contact with the surface of the water, and divides it into two halves. By shifting this partition to the right or the left, the surface on either side can be lengthened or shortened in any proportion."

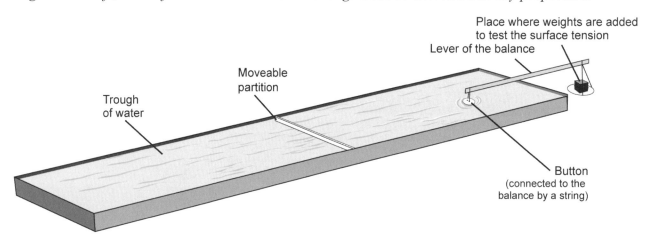

    While you may not have a rectangular tin trough on hand, you could try using water containers of varying size. Measure the surface area of the top of each container in units of centimeters squared (cm^2). Fill the containers to the brim with water, then test how much weight is required to remove the button from each. Record your results and then make a graph by hand or using a computer spreadsheet. The data set is "weight versus surface area." The units for weight could be, for example, number of plastic beads or number of paper clips.

4. Put together a talk about Agnes Pockels' life for younger students. Demonstrate your balance during the talk.

Researching Energy Sources

Do you know where your electricity comes from? Do you know what kind of power plant produces it? In this research project, you will investigate energy sources used to generate electricity. Each group in the class will research one type of power plant. When all the groups have completed their work, the class will review and discuss the information. Each group will be responsible for providing evidence that demonstrates the pros and cons of their energy source.

The final goal of this project is for your class to determine the most efficient, cost-effective, and environmentally safe method for generating electricity.

Sources of energy for generating electricity include coal, oil, natural gas, nuclear, hydroelectric, solar, wind, and geothermal.

 **MATERIALS**

Where to find information on the Internet:		
www.energy.gov	www.fe.doe.gov/education/index.html	www.eere.energy.gov/biomass
www.ase.org	http://energy.inel.gov/renewable	www.eia.doe.gov
www.energy.ca.gov	www.ne.doe.gov	www.eren.doe.gov

DIRECTIONS ▶

1. Choose one of the energy sources listed in the introductory paragraph.

2. Make a list of facts about this energy source. Come up with at least 10 pros and 10 cons. Cover these topics:

   a. How much does it cost to build a power plant for generating energy using your source?

   b. How much does it cost to maintain this type of power plant?

   c. How much does the energy source cost to use?

   d. How energy-efficient is this source?

   e. How does the use of your energy source affect human health?

   f. What are the environmental issues associated with using your energy source?

   g. How long into the future is this source projected to last?

3. As you make your list, fill in details to explain each point.

4. Prepare a one-page handout for your classmates which summarizes each point.

5. Prepare a poster highlighting two or three of the most important things you would like classmates to remember about your energy source.

ACTIVITIES

1. Decide as a class how you would like to learn about all of the energy sources. Some ideas include:

•   Have each group make a five-minute presentation to the class.

•   Make a booklet for each student that contains the summary sheet from each group. Each student should come up with a list of three questions they have after reading the booklet. Then give each student an opportunity to ask one question of another group.

2. Once you are familiar with the pros and cons of each source, consider these three questions separately:

    a.   Which one is the most efficient for your area of the country?

    b.   Which one is most cost-effective?

    c.   Which one is the safest for your environment?

3. If you were part of a commission studying which type of power plant to build in your community, how would you balance these three concerns? Is there one source which is best in every category?

4. Come up with a final recommendation for the best energy source for your community. Your class might choose to:

•   Form new groups, each with one person who studied each energy source. Each group should act as a commission responsible for making a recommendation to your community.

•   Or, have each person submit a statement about the best overall energy source for your community. Your teacher can divide the class into groups of students who share the same conclusion. Then, hold a debate among the groups.

Building an Electric Circuit Game

Do you have a steady hand? This project involves creating the setup for a game that challenges your manual dexterity. Can you move a small loop of wire over a complicated maze without tripping the light bulb? Try it and see!

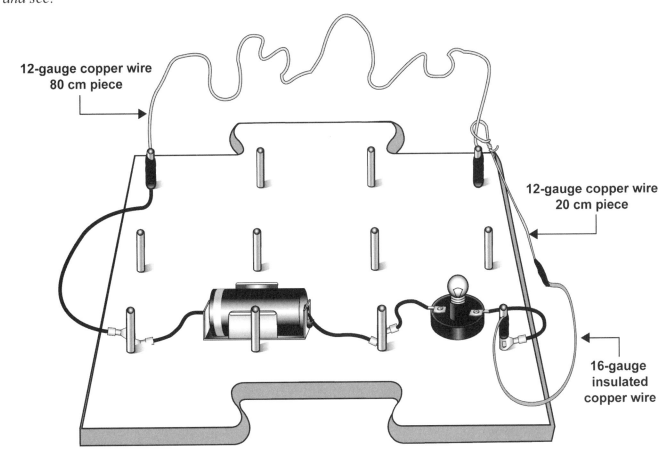

12-gauge copper wire 80 cm piece

12-gauge copper wire 20 cm piece

16-gauge insulated copper wire

MATERIALS ☑

- Electric Circuits Set: electricity table, one battery with holder, one light bulb with holder, one long connecting wire (brown)

- 1 meter of 12-gauge copper wire. Wire must not have an insulated coating. This wire can be purchased where picture hanging supplies are sold.

- 50 centimeter-long piece of 16-gauge insulated copper wire. This wire can be purchased at a hardware store.

- Electrical tape

- Wire stripper tool

- Permanent-ink marking pen

- Metric ruler or measuring tape

DIRECTIONS ▶

1. Place the battery, light bulb, and long connecting wire on the electricity table as shown in the diagram on the previous page.

2. Cut a 20-centimeter piece from one end of the 1 meter-long piece of 12-gauge copper wire.

3. Bend one end of the 20-cm piece in to a loop with a diameter no larger than a dime. The smaller the loop, the more challenging the game! Twist the wire to secure the loop. You have just constructed the wand for your game board.

4. Strip 2 cm of plastic coating from each end of the 50 cm length of 16 gauge wire. (Your teacher may help with this part).

5. Wrap one end of the exposed wire around the base of your wand and secure with electrical tape.

6. Wrap the other end of the exposed copper wire around the right front corner post of the electricity table. (The light bulb wire should also be connected to this post). Secure with electrical tape.

7. Measure 15 cm in from each end of your remaining 80 cm piece of 12 gauge copper wire. Mark the two spots with permanent ink. DO NOT cut the wire.

8. Make a 90° bend in the wire at each spot so that the wire is shaped like a wide, upside-down U.

9. Bend the long horizontal section of the wire into a series of hills and valleys (see illustration). Adjust the bends until the two 15 cm "legs" of the wire are 23 cm apart.

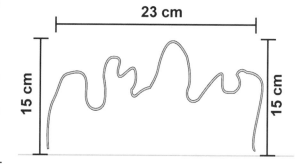

10. Place one of the 15-centimeter "legs" alongside the left, rear post of the electricity grid. The long connecting wire should be attached to this post. Secure the leg with electrical tape.

11. Slide the loop of your wand over the other leg of the 12-gauge wire.

12. Use electrical tape to secure this leg to the right, rear post of the electricity grid. Make sure that the tape covers the entire post.

13. Make sure that the loop in the wand will slide down the post. The loop should be placed in this position when the game is not in use.

14. Now you are ready to play! Using one hand, move the loop in the wand over the hills and valleys—but don't let the loop touch the copper wire! Try to make it all the way across without lighting the bulb.

Variation: Inexpensive buzzers can be purchased at electronic or hobby stores and placed in the circuit alongside the bulb.

Making a Model Maglev Train

Magnetically levitating (Maglev) trains use electromagnetic force to lift the train above the tracks. This system greatly reduces wear because there are few moving parts that carry heavy loads. It's also more fuel efficient, since the energy needed to overcome friction is greatly reduced. Although maglev technology is still in its experimental stages, many engineers believe it will become the standard for mass transit systems over the next 100 years.

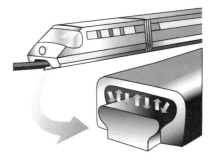

This project will give you an opportunity to create a model maglev train. You can even experiment with different means of providing power to your train.

MATERIALS

- 52 one-inch square magnets with north and south poles on the faces, rather than ends (found at hobby shops)
- One strip of 1/4-inch thick foam core, 24 inches long by 4 inches wide
- Two strips of 1/4-inch thick foam core, 24 inches long by 2.5 inches wide
- One strip of 1/4-inch thick foam core, 6 inches long by 3.75 inches wide
- Hot melt glue and glue gun
- Masking tape

DIRECTIONS

1. Cut a strip of masking tape 24 inches long. Press a line of 24 magnets onto the tape, north sides up.

2. Hold an additional magnet north side down and run it along the strip to make sure that the entire "track" will repel the magnet. Flip over any magnets that attract your test magnet.

3. Glue the magnet strip along one long side of the 24-by-4-inch foam core rectangle.

4. Repeat steps 1-2, then glue the second magnet strip along the opposite side to create the other track.

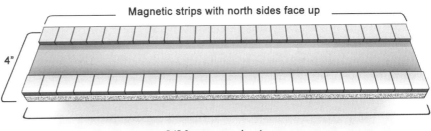

Magnetic strips with north sides face up

4"

24" foam core sheet

5. Place a bead of hot glue along the cut edge and attach one 24-by-2.5 inch foam core rectangle to form a short wall.

6. Repeat step 5 to form the opposite wall. This keeps the train from sliding sideways off the track.

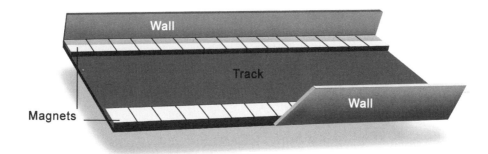

7. To create your train, glue the south side of a magnet to each corner of the small foam core rectangle.

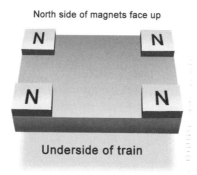

8. Turn the train over so that the north side of its magnets face the tracks. Place your train above the track and watch what happens!

ACTIVITIES

1. Experiment with various means to propel your train along the tracks. Consider using balloons, rubber bands and toy propellers, small motors (available at hobby stores) or even jet propulsion using vinegar and baking soda as fuel.

2. Build a longer, more permanent track using plywood shelving. Use Plexiglas for the front wall so that you can see the train floating above the track.

3. Find out how much weight your train can carry. Are some propulsion systems able to carry more weight than others? Why?

4. Have a design contest to see who can build the fastest train, or the train that can carry the most weight from one end of the track to the other.

Making Palm Pipes

A palm pipe is a musical instrument made from a simple material—PVC pipe. To play a palm pipe, you hit an open end of the pipe on the palm of your hand, causing the air molecules in the pipe to vibrate. These vibrations create the sounds that you hear.

MATERIALS

- 1 standard 10-foot length of 1/2 inch PVC pipe for 180°F water.
- Flexible meter stick
- PVC pipe cutter or a hacksaw
- Sandpaper
- Seven different colors of permanent markers for labeling pipes
- Simple calculator

DIRECTIONS ▶

1. Cut the PVC pipe into the lengths listed in the chart below. It works best if you measure one length, cut it, then make the next measurement. You may want to cut each piece a little longer than the given measurement so that you can sand out any rough spots and level the pipe without making it too short.

Number	Note	Length of pipe (cm)	Frequency (Hertz)
1	F	23.60	349
2	G	21.00	392
3	A	18.75	440
4	B flat	17.50	446
5	C	15.80	523
6	D	14.00	587
7	E	12.50	659
8	F	11.80	698
9	G	10.50	748
10	A	9.40	880
11	B flat	9.20	892
12	C	7.90	1049
13	D	7.00	1174
14	E	6.25	1318
15	F	5.90	1397

2. Lightly sand the cut ends to smooth any rough spots.

3. Label each pipe with the number, note, and frequency using a different color permanent marker.

4. Hit one open end of the pipe on the palm of your hand in order to make a sound.

ACTIVITIES

1. Try blowing across the top of a pipe as if you were playing a flute. Does the pipe sound the same as when you tap it on your palm? Why or why not?
   Safety note: Wash the pipes with rubbing alcohol or a solution of 2 teaspoons household bleach per gallon of water before and after blowing across them.

2. Take one of the longer pipes and place it in a bottle of water so that the top of the pipe extends above the top of the bottle. Blow across it like a flute. What happens to the tone as you raise or lower the pipe in the bottle?

3. Try making another set of palm pipes out of 1/2-inch copper tubing. What happens when you strike these pipes against your palm? What happens when you blow across the top? How does the sound compare with the plastic pipes?

4. At a hardware store, purchase two rubber rings for each copper pipe. These rings should fit snugly around the pipes. Place one ring on each end of each pipe, then lay them on a table. Try tapping the side of each pipe with different objects—wooden and stainless steel serving spoons, for example. How does this sound compare with the other sounds you have made with the pipes?

5. Try playing some palm pipe music with your classmates. Here are two tunes to get you started:

Happy Birthday

Melody	C	C	D	C	F	E		C	C	D	C	G	F
Harmony			A		A	B♭				B♭		B♭	A

Melody	C	C	C	A	F	E	D		B♭	B♭	A	F	G	F
Harmony			F		C	B♭					C			A

Twinkle Twinkle Little Star

Melody	F	F	C	C	D	D	C		B♭	B♭	A	A	G	G	F
Harmony	C	C	A	A	B♭	B♭	A		G	G	F	F	E	E	C

Melody	C	C	B♭	B♭	A	A	G		C	C	B♭	B♭	A	A	G
Harmony	A	A	G	G	F	F	C		A	A	G	G	F	F	C

Melody	F	F	C	C	D	D	C		B♭	B♭	A	A	G	G	F
Harmony	C	C	A	A	B♭	B♭	A		G	G	F	F	E	E	C

6. **Challenge:**

You can figure out the length of pipe needed to make other notes, too. All you need is a simple formula and your understanding of the way sound travels in waves.

To figure out the length of the pipe needed to create sound of a certain frequency, we start with the formula frequency = velocity of sound in air ÷ wavelength, or $f = v/\lambda$. Next, we solve the equation for λ: $\lambda = v/f$.

The fundamental frequency is the one that determines which note is heard. You can use the chart below to find the fundamental frequency of a chromatic scale in two octaves. Notice that for each note, the frequency doubles every time you go up an octave.

Once you choose the frequency of the note you want to play, you need to know what portion of the fundamental frequency's wavelength (S-shape) will fit inside the palm pipe.

To help you visualize the wave inside the palm pipe, hold the center of a flexible meter stick in front of you. Wiggle the meter stick to create a standing wave. This mimics a column of vibrating air in a pipe with two open ends. How much of a full wave do you see? If you answered one half, you are correct.

When a palm pipe is played, your hand closes one end of the pipe. Now use your meter stick to mimic this situation. Place the meter stick on a table top and use one hand to hold down one end of the stick. This represents the closed end of the pipe. Flick the other end of the meter stick to set it in motion. How much of a full wavelength do you see? Now do you know what portion of the wavelength will fit into the palm pipe?

One-fourth of the wavelength of the fundamental frequency will fit inside the palm pipe. As a result the length of the pipe should be equal to $1/4\lambda$, which is equal to $1/4(v/f)$.

In practice, we find that the length of pipe needed to make a certain frequency is actually a bit shorter than this. Subtracting a length equal to 1/4 of the pipe's inner diameter is necessary. The final equation, therefore, is: Length of pipe $= \dfrac{v}{4f} - \dfrac{1}{4}D$ where D represents the inner diameter of the pipe.

Given that the speed of sound in air (at 20°C) is 343 m/s and the inner diameter of the pipe is 0.0017 m, what is the length of pipe you would need to make the note B, with a frequency of 494 hertz? How about the same note one octave higher (frequency 988 hertz)? Make these two pipes so that you can play a C major scale.

Chromatic scale in two octaves (frequencies rounded to nearest whole number)												
Note	A	A#	B	C	C#	D	D#	E	F	F#	G	G#	A
Frequency (Hertz)	220	233	247	262	277	294	311	330	349	370	392	415	440
Frequency (Hertz)	440	466	494	523	554	587	622	659	698	740	784	831	880

7. What is the lowest note you could make with a palm pipe? What is the highest? Explain these limits using what you know about the human ear and the way sound is created by the palm pipe.

Building a Sundial

Measurement of days and months depends on the cycles between Earth and the moon and Earth and the sun. Therefore, it is not surprising that some of the first clocks were sundials based on the movement of shadows as the sun appeared to move across the sky. A sundial is a large timepiece on the ground. The "hand" of the clock to the right is a shadow created by an obelisk. You can build your own sundial, and then calibrate it so that you use it to accurately tell the time.

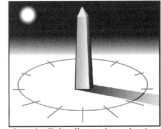

An obelisk allowed ancient Egyptians to divide up the day into parts.

MATERIALS

- Access to a library or the Internet
- Cardboard (manila) file folder
- Navigational compass
- Protractor
- Centimeter ruler, scissors, and clear tape

DIRECTIONS ▶

1. In order to build your sundial, you need to know the latitude of your city or town. To find your latitude, consult an atlas in your library, or use an Internet search engine. For example, to find the latitude of Ireton, Iowa, type: **latitude + Ireton + Iowa** into the search box. You will be directed one or more web sites providing the information you need. Ireton, Iowa is located at 43.039676° N latitude. For our purposes, round the latitude to the nearest whole degree.

2. Now, measure and cut out a 20-by-26 centimeter piece of the cardboard folder. First, draw one line dividing the piece in half. This will be the *noon line*. Then, draw a perpendicular line 2.5 centimeters from one edge: The place where the two lines intersect will be called the *vertex*.

3. Next you need to make the part of your sundial that casts a shadow. This part is called the **gnomon**. On another piece of the folder, mark off a baseline that is 10 centimeters long. Then, using your protractor, make an angle with this line that is equal to the angle of your particular location's latitude on Earth. If you lived in Ireton, Iowa you would make a 43° angle. Then, draw a second line, perpendicular to the baseline and making a right triangle. Write the angle for your latitude in the position shown on the diagram.

4. Cut out your gnomon. Then, attach the gnomon so that it is perpendicular to the base of the sundial. To keep the gnomon upright, cut out two rectangular tabs. Tape these to each side of the gnomon and fold them out in opposite directions. Then, tape them to the base of the sundial as shown.

5. Bring your sundial outside on a sunny day. Use a compass to help you point the noon line to the north.

MAKING THE SUNDIAL BASE

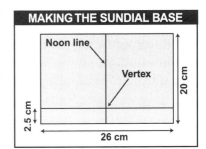

MAKING THE GNOMON

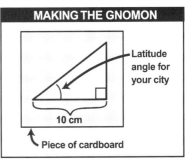

ATTACHING THE GNOMON

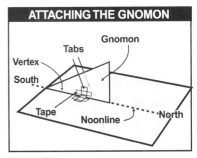

6. In order to tell the time accurately with your sundial, you need to calibrate it. You will need a few hours on a sunny afternoon to complete this part of the project.

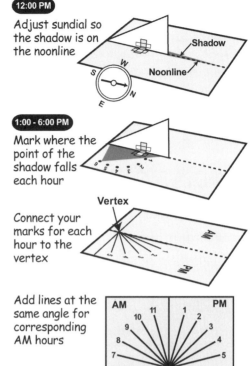

   a. Take your sundial outside at noon on a sunny day. Use a navigational compass to point the noon line on the sundial toward the north.

   b. Move the sundial slightly to the right or left until the point of the gnomon's shadow is resting on the noon line.

   c. Use the compass to determine the exact direction that the noon line is pointing, and write it down.

   d. Leave your sundial for exactly one hour. Go back and mark where point of the gnomon's shadow is located on the sundial. Write the time (1:00 pm) next to this mark.

   e. Repeat the fourth step five more times (until the actual time is 6:00 pm). You should have a mark for each hour after noon from 1:00 until 6:00.

   f. Take your sundial indoors. Use a ruler to connect each point to the vertex as shown. You have now calibrated your sundial to measure time from noon until 6:00 pm.

7. Use a protractor to measure the angle between the noon line and the 1:00 line. Measure the other angles from the noon line to each of the other marks and record all these angles in the table below.

8. To calibrate the morning hours, you will use the same angles you measured for the afternoon hours. The table below will help you determine which angle to use for each morning hour.

9. Test your sundial on another sunny day. To do this, make sure you use a compass to point the noon line in the direction you recorded earlier.

Afternoon hour	Angle from noon line	Corresponding morning hour
1:00 pm		11:00 am
2:00 pm		10:00 am
3:00 pm		9:00 am
4:00 pm		8:00 am
5:00 pm		7:00 am
6:00 pm		6:00 am

QUESTIONS ❓

   a. What variables affect the accuracy of your sundial? How could you improve your sundial so that you could tell the time within fifteen minutes?

   b. How do you think Daylight Savings Time will affect your sundial? How could you adjust the sundial to compensate?

   c. Use your imagination and materials you have around the house to build a more durable sundial.